THE DOG

STRUCTURE AND MOVEMENT

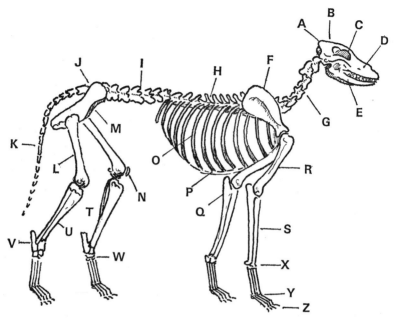

Fig. 1. Skeleton of dog Dolichocephalic (long head type)

A. *Occiput*	J. *Sacrum*	S. *Radius*
B. *Cranium*	K. *Coccygeal vertebrae*	T. *Fibula*
C. *Orbit*	L. *Femur*	U. *Tibia*
D. *Mandible*	M. *Pelvis*	V. *Os calcis*
E. *Maxilla*	N. *Patella*	W. *Tarsus*
F. *Scapula*	O. *Ribs*	X. *Carpus*
G. *Cervical vertebrae*	P. *Sternum*	Y. *Phalanges*
H. *Dorsal bones*	Q. *Ulna*	Z. *Pes or foot*
I. *Lumbar vertebrae*	R. *Humerus*	

THE DOG

STRUCTURE AND MOVEMENT

by

R. H. SMYTHE
M.R.C.V.S.

Illustrated by
STANLEY BENNETT

ARCO PUBLISHING COMPANY INC
New York

Published by
ARCO PUBLISHING COMPANY INC
219 Park Avenue South, New York, New York 10003

Printed in Great Britain

PREFACE

THIS book has been written mainly for *people* who keep dogs and wish to know a little more about them.

The term "people" includes, apart from the pet owners, breeders of dogs, exhibitors and judges, as well as the students, who seek information concerning the various breeds, their anatomical differences and the connection in each breed between conformation and movement.

The anatomical section is limited to salient features of importance to the subject in hand and omits all reference to arteries, veins, nerves and muscles, other than those which are concerned with surface anatomy and the matter of locomotion.

The illustrations of anatomical structures are entirely diagrammatic and intended to make the text more easy to understand.

CONTENTS

ILLUSTRATIONS

INTRODUCTION

In spite of the fact that their original ancestry was the same, dogs of today may be divided into those termed mongrels, the result of promiscuous breeding, and those regarded as " pure breeds ".

There are at least 250 recognized breeds of dog throughout the world including about 150 scheduled in Britain, 45 more or less confined to other countries, and another 45 indigenous breeds almost wholly contained within limited geographical areas, none of which so far have been exported to foreign lands.

With a very few exceptions the so-called " pure breeds " have in their genetic make-up just as many differing types or varieties as the average mongrel. As an example, one well-known pure breed, which shall be nameless, has eventually been standardized after the mating together over a number of years of fourteen recognized breeds.

Most of the existing breeds have been produced by what is termed " selective breeding ".

In the earlier days when attempts were being made to develop existing breeds or produce new ones, dogs and bitches of similar or entirely different type and shape were mated together and any pair of their offspring, male and female, which possessed desirable qualities whether of conformation, temperament or both, were again mated.

As it was believed that inbreeding induced weakness in the progeny specimens derived by this process, those most nearly approaching the ideal being aimed at, would often be "back-mated " to one of the original parents, or more often, perhaps, to another specimen of the parental breed which might or might not be related to one or both of the original parents.

Many years ago, before dog shows became popular, most breeders' efforts were directed towards producing dogs of a type and size suited to the special kind of work to be demanded from them.

A dog may have been needed that would guard premises and property, hunt game, act as a beast of burden or herd goats, sheep or cattle.

Within certain limits the type of work demanded some fairly definite pattern of conformation, together with suitable size and temperament. It soon became evident, however, that among working dogs the possession of apparently ideal conformation did not guarantee a corresponding degree of usefulness, unless the conformation was coupled in the same individual with the right temperament and a high degree of intelligence.

In other words the working dog required not only the shape and physique essential to the job, but also it needed the temperament which would permit it to accept human direction and derive pleasure from putting its master's wishes into execution.

It was discovered, too, that the dog possessing these mental characteristics would display greater enthusiasm and put far more effort into its work.

Fig. 2. Scottish Terrier

An achondroplastic type with large head and stunted limbs. Note the relative proportion in size of the limb bones. (Diagrammatic)

Further experience has also made it clear that even among members of the same breed, the possessor of the whole range of show points may be of less value for work than the throw-out. Although, for example, there are Cocker spaniels and Retrievers which are able to win prizes in the showring, as well as work in the field, it is well known among shooting men that few of the very good gun dogs they value highly would ever be looked at in a novice class.

Nowadays, apart from dogs engaged in hunting, shooting and racing, and those actively employed in leading the blind, ability to carry out a set task comes a bad second to the ability to win prizes in the show-ring purely on the strength of conformation and movement.

Every breed or variety of a breed, has its own set standard of conformation and physical excellence. This may vary for each particular breed; one needs long legs, another short; another needs a long muzzle and yet another must have a flat face and little muzzle at all. So much do dogs differ from one another in appearance—more so than in any other species of quadruped—that a visitor from another planet might be forgiven for imagining that a Chihuahua and a Great Dane were representatives of two entirely different species.

The mongrel, the product of countless generations of chance matings, has survived in the face of considerable opposition because it possessed a reliable temperament and a lot of intelligence. Mankind has eliminated all the mongrels which exhibited bad manners or inability to put up with man and his peculiarities, and the survivors—the lucky ones—have inherited the ability to tolerate domestication and to enjoy the good things of life in return for unswerving loyalty and a desire to protect the territory they share with their (pack) bosses against intruders upon their privacy.

It is a fact that temperament—good or bad—is frequently hereditary and that of late years the appearance of uncertain temper and a tendency to snap at or bite humans, is making an appearance in certain breeds usually regarded as friendly and docile.

It is up to breeders to pay attention to temperament just as much as to conformation. Judges, too, should severely penalize dogs which exhibit anti-social tendencies, however good they may be as regards structure and movement.

The characteristics which need elimination are unnatural shyness and distrust.

It may be queried why a book dealing with conformation and structure should commence with a warning note regarding temperament.

The reason is that conformation, especially when faulty, can easily be viewed even from the ringside but faulty temperament can often be concealed by an expert handler during the short time the dog is in the ring. It is useless to produce a dog with the desired conformation unless it is accompanied by a pleasing temperament and the ability to associate safely with mankind.

It is a fact, one to which a good deal of attention has been drawn recently, that many of the people who keep, breed and exhibit dogs, have little knowledge of their basic anatomy or of the structural features underlying the physical formation insisted upon in the standards laid down for any particular breed.

Nor do many of them—and this includes some of the accepted judges—know, when they handle a dog in or outside the showring, the nature of the structures which give rise to the varying contours of the body, or why certain types of conformation are desirable and others harmful.

With all due respect, the same may sometimes be written regarding those whose duty it is to formulate standards designed to preserve the usefulness or encourage the welfare of the recognized breeds.

The few books dealing with canine anatomy available to the veterinary profession are far too detailed and complicated for private use and would prove unintelligible to the lay reader. To overcome this and fill a longfelt need, this present volume has been written for the use of the many breeders, exhibitors and judges, as well as for R.A.N.A. students and also for the many who keep dogs solely as pets, and wish to know more than they do at present about the structure of the dog and particularly regarding those parts of its body hidden beneath the skin.

To provide this information, or even to arrange it in such a way that it can be referred to whenever the need arises, the book has been written so far as is possible in simple language. Although not pretending to cover the whole of the anatomical field which would require several volumes, an effort has been made to include all the main features which concern the ordinary reader and exhibitor, as well as every breeder. Especial attention has been drawn to the differences which are present in breeds as unlike as the Bullmastiff and the Chihuahua. This is especially necessary in the case of the dog, in which with the help of man, more than three hundred separate varieties have emanated from the original wolf-like ancestors. There is probably no other species of animal in which anything like the same number of dissimilar types exists. A man is very like another man, whether he be white, black or yellow, and the same applies to the horse.

A carthorse and a Shetland pony may vary greatly in size but the skeleton of the second is merely a perfect miniature of the first.

In the dog family, bodies are of entirely different shapes and designs, while skulls, although possessing some similarities may be unlike in the relative proportions of their respective parts.

This also applies to the limb bones and vertebrae, since owing to the fact that mutations are eagerly accepted as the foundations of a new breed, the dogs of today may be squarely-built animals standing three-feet-high or they may be three-feet-long and a foot high, with limbs so short that their bellies trail upon the ground. Many of the abnormalities accepted today in show dogs as special breed characteristics result from corresponding abnormality of the pituitary and thyroid glands and their secretions into the blood stream.

The illustrations throughout the book characterize the bones and other parts of the dog's anatomy as they occur in many different breeds but in order that they may serve their purpose and be readily understood, many of them must be accepted as being diagrammatic rather than as correct in every minute detail.

This book is intended for the lay reader and the student rather than for the veterinary surgeon who has already received more detailed instruction in all the phases of anatomy. It is possible, however, that veterinary students who have learned their anatomy from the study of one particular type of dog, or from a single skeleton, or from a limited number of dissection subjects, may benefit from this simple description of the differences existent between the very dissimilar breeds. It is also likely that the book may be useful to the many students now training to enter the veterinary field in the role of members of the British Animal Nursing Auxiliaries Association.

In the following chapters we will consider many parts of the body and discuss the variations present in different breeds, as well as the influence such differences exert upon a dog's comfort, its well-being and utility.

THE DOG

STRUCTURE AND MOVEMENT

B

CHAPTER ONE

THE HEAD

THERE has ever been a tendency among all who essay to judge the respective merits of dogs to look first at the head and pay far more attention to it than to all the rest of the body.

This may be done quite unconsciously since the head and face are the most obvious seats of expression and a dog possessing a plain head, accompanied by a woebegone countenance, may fail to arouse admiration or enthusiasm in its beholder.

In consequence, one owning a perfect head and expression is far more likely to be in the money, even if it possesses a dubious body, than when the converse is the case.

Human nature being what it is, the chances are that, rightly or wrongly, the head will continue to attract the most attention and that the dog fancier like many in other walks of life will often, perhaps too often, be led astray and be prepared to overlook minor faults and give full marks to a pretty face and expression.

Before discussing heads further it is essential to draw attention to the fact that there are two very different types found in the dog family together with an intermediate variety which has resulted from interbreeding, mainly at the instigation of mankind, since the two types appear to have associated very little while in a state of nature or prior to domestication.

In modern times the mating together of the two types has resulted in the production of a number of new breeds.

The two differing head shapes may be described briefly as long and short. In scientific language the long head is referred to as *dolichocephalic* and the short head as *brachycephalic*. The intermediate variety is classed as *mesocephalic*.

It would really be more accurate to speak of a short face rather than a short head since in most instances the reduction in length occurs between nose and lips rather than between the eyes and poll.

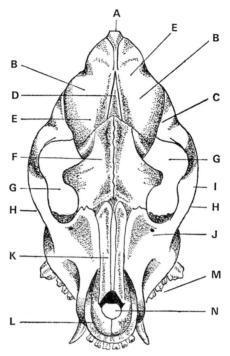

Fig. 3. Skull of Bullmastiff (from above) (Mesocephalic)

A. *Occipital bone* F. *Frontal bone* K. *Nasal bones*
B. *Parietal bone*   G. *Orbit*   L. *Premaxilla*
B. *and C. Temporal fossa* H. *Zygoma*   M. *Premolars*
D. *Sagittal crest*   I. *Zygomatic arch* N. *Incisor foramen*
E. *Cranium*   J. *Superior maxilla*

The skull depicted belongs to the mesocephalic type, being that of a Bullmastiff.

The muzzle is shorter than in the long-headed dolicocephalic breeds but longer than in the very short-faced brachycephalic breeds, which include such as the Pug and the Pekingese.

The cranial division of all three types is somewhat similar apart from the fact that in most of the brachycephalic skulls the cranial capacity is relatively slightly greater than in the long-headed skulls, as compared with the bodyweights of their previous owners.

The main differences between the long-faced and short-faced skulls lies in the relative lengths of the superior maxilla, (J) the nasal bones, and the premaxilla.

In Pekingese and Pugs the nasal bones are greatly reduced in length and there is a similar shortening of the bones underlying the anterior portion of the underside of the skull,

Some of the long heads may be twelve inches in length and of this six to eight inches may represent jaws and the remainder skull, including the cranium or braincase.

In the short-faced dogs the distance between the eyes and the tip of the nose may be less than once inch, while the skull and cranium above eye level may be wider and equally as long as that present in one of the long-faced varieties.

The reduction in length occurs in the jaw bones, particularly in those of the upper jaw, and the nasal bones, as well as in some of the bones which help to form the base of the skull.

We will discuss this more fully presently.

It is usual, too, for the short-faced types to have wider skulls than the long-faced with excellent development of the cranium and of the zygomatic arch, a lateral projection of bone which protects and encloses the eye, as well as providing an increased surface for the attachment of the muscles which operate the jaws.

---

commencing with the sphenoid and vomer bones and extending forwards to include the palatine bones and, of course, the whole of the superior maxilla.

The orbit shows little difference in the various skull types excepting that in the brachycephalic heads the orbit is wider and the portion which contains the eyeball lies nearer the midline of the skull, since the nasal bones occupy less space as regards their width and length. This permits the dog to enjoy something much more nearly approaching frontal vision than is possible in the long-headed types.

In the long-headed dogs the zygomatic arch is much less marked and the malar portion of the zygoma is much straighter than in the shorter-faced varieties.

In these, too, the sagittal crest which runs down the centre of the cranium, overlying the junction of the parietal bones, is usually much more prominent, although there are breed differences which may be ascertained by studying the respective breed standards.

On either side of the sagittal process and overlying the parietal bones, is a recess into which the fibres of the temporal muscle are attached. These muscles provide a slight elevation of the skin surface covering them.

This recess in the upper surface of the skull is known as the temporal fossa and it may reappear in the live dog when emaciation or certain types of nerve disease have reduced the size of the temporal muscle which normally fills the fossa. This muscle is inserted at its lower end into the coronoid process of the mandible (lower jaw). See Figs 9 and 10.

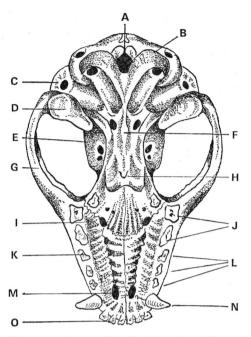

Fig. 4. Under surface of Skull of Cavalier King Charles
(Mesocephalic)

A. Foramen magnum
B. Condyle of occipital bone
C. Entrance to middle ear
D. Glenoid fossa (articulation with lower jaw)
E. Basilar process
F. Presphenoid bone
G. Zygomatic arch (malar bone)
H. Vomer bone
I. Palatine bone
J. Carnassial tooth (4th. premolar and 1st molar)
K. Palatine groove
L. 1st., 2nd., 3rd. premolars
M. Incisor cleft
N. Canine tooth
O. Incisor teeth

On the under surface of the mesocephalic skull depicted (from a Cavalier King Charles Spaniel), note the foramen magnum (A) through which the spinal cord, continuous with the medulla, emerges from the cranium and travels through the neural canals of adjoining vertebrae, throughout the length of the spine as far as the sacrum. After this point sensation is conveyed by caudal material containing nerve tissue.

The foramen magnum is bounded on either side by a convex articular process known as the occipital condyle. Each articulates with a corresponding articular cavity on the front of the atlas, the first of the seven cervical bones.

In the midline of the under surface of the skull and beneath (or behind) the foramen magnum, a thick rod of bone—the basilar process—descends vertically to articulate with the body of the sphenoid bone.

It is the basilar process, usually in

It is evident that the short-faced dogs arose originally as mutations from the long-faced varieties of wild dogs, though when and where is unknown. The long-faces hunted their own food but the short-heads having short legs and somewhat inefficient jaws were compelled to behave as pacifists relying mainly upon a little scavengering to provide themselves with food. It was fortunate perhaps with an eye to survival, that they also possessed good nature coupled with certain gastronomic virtues which enabled them to act as children's pets and bedwarmers until such time as they had acquired the necessary fatness and succulence to provide a delect-

---

conjunction with the vomer, which becomes fractured as the result of concussion, frequently in collisions with cars.

The degree of curvature of the zygoma and the resulting width or narrowness of the orbit, is seen better from below the skull. The zygoma is made up of three separate bones and their points of union can be seen. These are the frontal, malar and lachrymal bones. Above, the zygoma joins up with the squamous temporal bone. The bulk of the bone is malar. Below it merges into the superior maxilla. At about the middle of its length it presents a tubercle on its medial edge which corresponds with a similar tubercle on the frontal bone. These do not meet and so an open orbit remains. Nevertheless, during life, the two tubercles give attachment to a fibrous ligament which bridges the space and in theory at least, divides the orbit into an ocular portion housing the eyeball, and a temporal portion which gives passage to the ramus of the lower jaw. The under surface of the zygoma, at its upper end, carries on either side an oblong articular surface which accommodates the articular surface of the mandible (the lower jaw).

A little below the occipital condyles and between these and the upper end of the zygoma, lies a prominence known as the auditory bulla, part of the petrous temporal bone; the interior of the bulla is filled with honeycomb air cells and spaces, all in communication with the eardrum or tympanum.

Emerging laterally from each of these two bullae are bony channels which lead into the tympanum and with this exception are continuous with the middle and internal ear.

These two bony portions of the auditory canal leave the membranous portion of the ear canal at almost a right angle and it is this which makes it so difficult to completely examine the ear passage unless one is provided with special apparatus for the purpose.

The occipital bone lying at the peak of the cranium, varies in its degree of development in the different breeds. In many of the gundogs, the Pointer for example, it is very noticeable and in the majority of gundogs and in hounds it is generally fairly prominent. In the short-faced breeds it is not very visible and generally speaking, it is well-developed only in dogs with drooping ears.

able roast. When and how this remarkable mutation from long faces to short came about has given rise to a great deal of conjecture and numerous theories.

The suggestion made above may account for their rather miraculous survival in the face of great disadvantages but it does not explain how the changes in shape arose.

One is that the normal development of the embryo in the womb of the bitch became disturbed by radiation arising during the world's upheavals. This may have retarded the course of gestation to an extent when the young were born at an incomplete stage of development and before the bones of the head had attained their normal final stage. Although the possibility of exposure to radiation cannot reasonably be disregarded, the theory of *foetalisation* (incomplete development) is disputed.

Another theory is that the condition arose from malfunction of the pituitary and thyroid glands, also possibly caused by radiation. The short-faced dogs were unable to chase and kill their own food, especially as their legs were also shortened, and this may have been one of the reasons why dogs first adopted humanity.

The brachycephalic head is remarkable for the width of the zygomatic arch responsible for the broadening of the skull and also for the frontal eye placement which goes with this increase in width. In these short-faced dogs the eyes face forward in much the same way that our own do, while in the long-faced varieties the eyes are set obliquely, and a little to the side of the head, usually at an angle of thirty degrees with a line drawn longitudinally through the midline of the head, i.e., midway between the eyes and ears.

The mating together of the long-faced and short-faced varieties almost invariably produces puppies of intermediate type, often with the advantage of sufficient jaw length to produce a very efficient " bite " and without the disadvantages involving breathing and swallowing so commonly seen in the truly brachycephalic breeds.

The Boxer and the Bullmastiff are examples and however one may be attracted to the King Charles spaniel, few would deny that the Cavalier has considerable advantages over it, afforded by extra jaw length and the possession of a reasonable degree of prolongation of its nasal bones.

In spite of the fact that dogs' heads differ enormously in outline, shape and size, there are, however, certain features common to them all, even if the connection is sometimes hard to trace, as when one compares the skull of a long-headed dog such as an Alsatian with that of a short-faced dog such as the Pekingese. The results of crossing the long-faced varieties with the short-faced will be discussed later.

There is in every case one exceedingly important structure present in every dog's skull located between the upper level of the eyes and the peak of the head (the *occiput*).

This is the *cranium*, the braincase, made up from the bones which surround and support the cranial cavity. It contains the brain.

Incidentally, the cranium contained within a short-faced (brachycephalic) skull, such as one encounters in the Pekingese or in a Bulldog, Griffon or Pug, for examples, may be even better developed and of greater capacity and therefore enclosing a larger brain, relatively, than that present in the larger long-faced breeds such as the Alsatian, making due allowance, of course, for the difference in weight of the two dogs.

This does not necessarily imply that the Alsatian is less intelligent than the Pekingese, or vice versa, since brain efficiency depends largely upon the thickness and distribution of the " thatch " of *grey matter* covering the underlying primitive brain and not so much upon the actual size of the whole brain.

The grey matter, which carries the nerve structures and the main lines of communication between the brain and the different parts of the body, is spread out over, as well as buried or inserted into the substance of the brain in a continuous layer, forming ridges and depressions on its surface. These are referred to as *convolutions*.

The disposition of the grey matter in these convolutions may best be compared with what would happen if one were to wrap a ball of putty in a handkerchief much too large to cover it, then poke the surface of the handkerchief into various parts of the putty with the handle of a spoon or a small spatula, until all the handkerchief was used up, and then give the whole a good squeeze in the hands.

The larger the handkerchief the more " convolutions " would be formed on the surface of the mass and if one were now to cut through its centre with a sharp knife, one would see how a brain looked when similarly divided.

The putty would represent the original primitive brain and the handkerchief and its buried folds would take the place of the grey matter, the important part of the brain. (*See Fig. 7*)

Look now, too, at *Figs. 3, 4 and 7* and note how the cranium is situated in the skull, in the latter.

The brain is made up of a large anterior section, the *cerebrum*, the seat of knowledge, and a smaller hind portion the *cerebellum*, concerned largely with co-ordination of movement and with balance.

Lying beneath and behind this is the *medulla*, a continuation of the brain connecting it with the *spinal cord*, which travels down the body through each of the spinal bones (vertebrae) giving off nerves at regular intervals on the way.

The interior of the cranial cavity is roughly divided or " waisted " to accommodate these three sections of the brain.

A great many separate bones enter into the formation of the skull and to simplify matters the skull may be divided into *cranium* and *face*.

Apart from the cranium, the remainder of the skull is concerned with the application of many of the body functions as well as the use of the various senses including sight, hearing, taste and skin sensation, together with the essential acts of breathing and swallowing and the production of vocal sounds. The central brain acts as the receiving station for stimuli conveyed through the sense organs and converts these into mental impressions which convey meaning to the animal.

The individual bones which constitute the skull, apart from those which enter into the formation of the lower jaw, are with one or two exceptions thin, flattened or curved plates of bone of definite shape, united by closely applied edges, the lines of apposition being commonly referred to as " *sutures* ".

During the first year of life most of these sutures remain cartilaginous in nature so that the separate bones are able to alter their relative size and shape during the time in which the puppy is growing into its final adult formation.

Some of the cranial bones such as the *occipital bone* which forms the crest of the skull, fuse before birth with the *parietal bones* lying immediately below it, while the *temporal bones* which form part of the lateral walls of the cranium, similarly become united at an early age.

This is somewhat in contrast with the overgrown human cranium, some of the sutures of which may not become completely replaced by bone before middle age.

The two central bones forming the roof of the cranium are known as the parietal bones. (*See Fig. 3*)

In most breeds these unite in the middle line of the head and produce a raised ridge known as the *sagittal crest*.

In the Chihuahua and in some of the brachycephalic breeds the sagittal crest is absent or poorly developed. Usually in the modern Chihuahua the sagittal crest is absent and a gap exists between the sutures of the parietal and frontal bones, filled only by membrane. This greatly resembles the anterior fontanelle of the human infant but in the Chihuahua it usually persists throughout life. Pressure with the tip of the finger upon this area can be dangerous though, as a rule, as the gap is centrally placed, the pressure falls upon the longitudinal fissure which exists between the two halves of the cerebrum in the middle line and not directly upon the frontal lobes.

In the long-faced breeds (dolichocephalic) and the short-faced (brachycephalic), one encounters a great many very apparent structural differences which will be discussed later. Taking a long-faced breed such as the Alsatian, the cranium may be regarded as possessing a roof, lateral walls and two extremities. The bones are disposed as follows : —

Upper end

The occipital and interparietal. *Single bones*

Roof

The parietal and frontal bones. *Double bones.*

The lateral surfaces of the roof form the internal boundaries of the *temporal fossae* which will be discussed presently. The bones forming the roof are all thin apart from the *occipital*, the highest one, the " peak " of the skull, which is thick and strong and in some breeds such as the hunting dogs and gundogs which work with noses to the ground, particularly prominent and solid. (*See Fig. 3*)

Lateral walls of the cranium

These are made up from the occipital, temporal, parietal and frontal bones which become integrated below with the floor of the cranium without visible sutures.

The floor of the cranium

This is formed by the basilar process of the occipital bone and the sphenoid bone. (*See Fig 4*)

In some of the more pronounced short-faced breeds the front end of the sphenoid bone is poorly developed and the flattened plate of the palatine bone which supports the roof of the mouth (the hard palate) may be incomplete on the midline, giving rise to *cleft palate*. This is regarded as a genetical fault, an autosomal recessive, confined to certain strains but by the very nature of the shortened face in brachycephalic breeds it may even occur irrespective of strain, although possibly rather more frequently when the degree of deformity has become excessively marked.

The *vomer bone* which lies farther forward along the middle line of the lower surface of the skull, although not a part of the cranium, cuts off the nasal passages from the mouth by acting in the form of a wedge dividing the right chamber of the nostrils from the left. In the more pronounced brachycephalic skulls, particularly in that of the Bulldog, the bone may be incomplete or more deeply notched at its anterior end than is normal and this interferes with the suspension of the soft palate giving rise to difficulty in breathing, more marked in warm weather. Such a condition is often farther complicated by faulty development of the sphenoid bone, a common occurrence in many short-faced individuals. (*See Fig. 4*)

The *upper end of the cranium* is pierced by the *foramen magnum*, the large canal through which the brain and spinal cord enter into communication.

The *lower end of the cranium* is closed by the ethmoid bone and its perforated (cribriform) plate.

The Cranium (or Braincase) (See Figs. 3 and 4)

This occupies in some cases only a small part of the entire width of the skull. The proportion is variable and depends almost entirely upon the breed of dog and whether it owns a long or a short face. In the latter the *zygomatic arch* greatly increases the apparent width of the brow. We will enlarge on this topic presently.

The cranium rests in the centre of a cavity referred to as the *temporal fossa*, half of which lies on the one side and the remainder on the opposite side of the cranium. This cavity is continuous below in the dog—but not in all other animals—with the *orbital fossa* which contains and protects the eyeball. (*See Figs. 3 and 6*)

In the horse and ox for example, the two fossae are separated by a bridge of bone so that the upper half—the temporal fossa—is distinct from the lower orbital fossa and for this reason these two animals are said to have a " *closed orbit* ".

The dog on the other hand is said to possess an " *open orbit* ". Open orbits are also present in the pig and the cat.

In either case whether the orbit be open or closed, it contains the eyeball, while the upper cavity, the temporal fossa, gives passage to the upper end of the lower jaw (*the mandible*). (*See Figs. 3, 5 and 6*)

The outer boundary of these two fossae is a continuous arch of bone formed mainly from the highly developed *zygoma* of the *malar bone.* (*See Figs. 3, 4 and 6*) It is known as the *zygomatic arch.*

This very conspicuous and prominent zygomatic arch, as previously mentioned, varies a great deal in the degree of its curvature in different breeds. In the short-faced brachycephalic breeds it may amount almost to a semi-circle while in the long-faced

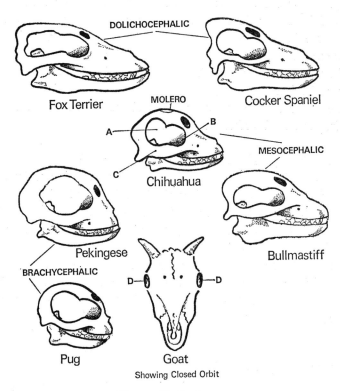

Fig. 5. Skull shapes

A. Orbit
B. Portion containing eye-
ball
C. Zygomatic arch
D. Closed Orbit

The black spot on each skull represents the position of the frontal sinus

There is greater variation in the skulls of dogs than in any other species of animal. The reason is that from one, or possibly a few pairs of ancestors, man has now harboured, and in many instances created, over 300 breeds, all differing in numerous respects and not least, in skull shape.

The main factors which give rise to this variation are differences in the curvature of the zygoma; degree of development of the occiput and of the sagittal crest; the size of the frontal sinuses which decide whether or not the " stop " will influence the type of head; and what is very important, the degree of development or lack of development of the nasal bones, and finally, the very important matter of jaw length in relation to the remainder of the skull.

The shape of the forehead may vary a great deal as will be seen by glancing at the illustration.

The terriers usually have flat foreheads, often with some central ridging dolichocephalic breeds such as the Alsatian, Borzoi and Fox Terriers, the zygoma is a much straighter bone, lying nearly parallel to the outer wall of the cranium and so the zygomatic arch is correspondingly less curved and capacious. It is this variable degree of curvature of the zygoma which decides the width of the dog's forehead and it must not be imagined—as so many people do—that a dog is likely to be more intelligent because it owns a wide forehead. The common remark that such a head " *gives room for more brains* ", is based on an utterly false foundation.

The head of a Labrador or a St. Bernard is wide because the zygoma is strong and *arched*, but the extreme relative width is encountered in the Bulldog, Pekingese and Griffon, while an intermediate type is seen in many of the breeds which are made up from crosses of breeds carrying the two types of head, long and short. These include the Bullmastiff, the Bull terriers, Cavaliers, and the Boxer. In certain breeds such as the Boston Terrier, the brachycephalic type of skull remains dominant but without undue exaggeration.

---

arising from development of the sagittal crest. Some of the toy breeds have apple heads and in others the apple head is regarded as a fault.

In some breeds the ears are set close together, in others they are farther apart. In many breeds the ears are erect, in others they fall or lie flat against the cheeks or they may be semi erect. Although this has little to do with skull shape, nevertheless certain types of skull are usually linked with certain types of ears.

The size and capacity of the open orbit of the dog depends largely upon the degree of straightness or curvature of the zygoma but in addition this affects eye placement and usually the straighter the zygoma, or putting it another way, the less the degree of curvature, the more obliquely are the eyes situated in relation to the midline

of the skull. Indirectly, the shape of the zygoma also influences ear placement in some degree. As a general rule, the eyes and ears work in unison and the ears when upright, usually are aimed at the point which is being viewed by the eyes. When the eyes are set obliquely and wide apart the ears tend to droop but when the eyes in a prick-eared breed are placed more or less frontally, the ears tend to lie closer together.

In the Chihuahua there is very frequently present a small aperture centrally placed, a little above eye level, in the upper surface of the cranium. This overlies the longitudinal fissure between the two halves of the fore-brain, the cerebrum; and pressure from fingers may cause signs of brain damage when the aperture in the skull is particularly large.

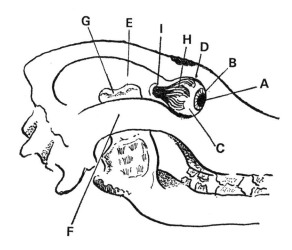

Fig. 6. The eye within the Orbit

A. Pupil behind cornea
B. Iris
C. Sclera
D. Muscles controlling movements of eyeball
E. Coronoid process of lower jaw
F. Zygoma
G. Temporal fossa
H. Orbit or orbital fossa
I. Optic foramen, through which the optic nerve leaves the cranium

As previously mentioned, the orbit is incompletely divided in the dog into two parts, an anterior, smaller portion which contains the eyeball and a posterior portion which provides space for the coronoid process of the maxilla to move freely. On the outer aspect of the orbit the space is bounded by the zygoma, and the capacity of the orbit depends largely upon the degree of curvature in the zygomatic arch.

In forming the bony wall of the orbit the frontal bone occupies the greater part, but the lachrymal bone assists, together with a narrow strip of the palatine.

The entrance to the orbit is not entirely encircled by bone so far as the portion containing the eyeball is concerned. The remainder is completed by the orbital ligament, a fibrous cord which joins up the two bony projections, one from the frontal bone and the other from the zygoma itself.

In the depth of the orbit is a pad of fat, the amount of which may vary considerably according to the bodily condition of the dog. This pad of fat keeps the eye in position with relation to the palpebral fissure (the space between the eyelids) and has a considerable effect upon whether the eye is full and prominent or sunken in the eye socket.

The separation between the eyeball and the part which acts as a receptacle for the ramus of the lower jaw is completed by the stout fibrous periorbita. This is a conical sheath with its apex adherent to the borders of the optic foramen and its base fused with the orbital ligament and with the

One might be partially excused for imagining that the cranium was larger in the wide-skulled breeds than in the longer narrower heads, but this length and narrowness has resulted from selective breeding and does nothing to negative the general rule regarding the size of the cranium. The exceptions one has in mind are the Borzoi and Afghan in which the cranial capacity is lower, weight for weight, than in most other breeds.

In the other direction the highest cranial capacities, again weight for weight, are found in the smaller brachycephalic skulls, notably that of the Griffon and Pekingese.

It must not, however, be concluded that the intelligence quota of a Borzoi is therefore lower than that of the smaller dog. The kind of life expected of either breed is totally different, and the mental capacity is—or should be—related to the requirement of each in its normal modern environment. We humans are apt to measure an animal's intelligence in accordance with how it adapts itself to the *human* way of living.

As previously mentioned, in a good many breeds, especially in those which possess a narrow zygomatic arch and a correspondingly narrow head, a ridge of bone runs centrally and longitudinally down the cranium. At its upper end it is prolonged to join the occipital crest and at its lower it reaches the inferior limit of the parietal bones. This ridge is known as the *sagittal crest*. It strengthens the cranium and provides attachment for the temporal muscles.

The sagittal crest has a number of functions apart from playing

---

periosteum covering the bony orbital margin. The eyeball is therefore fully enclosed in this conical sac and completely separated from the rest of the orbital cavity.

The direction in which the orbit lies is not entirely parallel with the centre line of the cranium even in those breeds which most nearly approach frontal vision.

In most of the long-headed breeds the axis runs in a dorsal and lateral direction from the optic foramen, so that the two axes carried backwards, would enclose an angle of seventy-nine degrees.

The nearest to a parallel exists in the Poodles and the brachycephalic varieties.

C

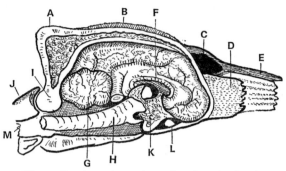

Fig. 7. Section of cranium showing the brain

A. Occiput
B. Sagittal crest
C. Frontal sinus
D. Ethmoid bone
E. Nasal bone over-
    lying turbinate
F. Corpus callosum within
    cerebrum
G. Cerebellum
H. Medulla
I. Articulation of skull
    and atlas (1st. cervical)
J. Atlas
K. Pituitary body
L. Optic chiasma
M. Foramen magnum

The brain is ovoid in shape, the hinder end being the larger. This portion contains the cerebellum, the medulla oblongata and part of the cerebrum.

The front portion, smaller and more compressed, contains the greater part of the cerebral hemispheres, capped by the olfactory bulbs. Looking at the brain from above one sees little more than the two halves of the cerebrum, though a small part of the cerebellum can be observed together with a small part of the medulla oblongata. It is the medulla which merges into the spinal cord and thus makes its way through the foramen magnum, the large orifice at the rear end of the skull, to pass down through the neural canal in the body of each succeeding vertebra.

Immediately in front of the medulla is a broad, transverse band, the pons, which joins up laterally with the cerebrum.

Beneath the brain the two optic tracts approach one another and finally blend at the optic chiasma (in the form of a cross). The brain receives its blood supply from three main sources, the single basilar artery, which travels up through the vertebral canal and passes into the cranium through the foramen magnum; and by the two (right and left) internal carotid arteries.

The brain is made up of a nucleus of white material covered with what may be described as a thatch of grey matter, composed of intertwined nerve cells. The grey material follows all the projections, kinks and crevices—the convolutions—of the brain into their depths, and it is the proportion of grey material as compared with the white core, which decides the degree of intelligence exhibited. Actually, the size and weight of the brain may be no criterion unless the grey material is present in sufficient quantity. The result of this intrusion of grey matter into the depths of the brain while covering the white core, is that when one makes a section of the brain, even at its greatest depth, one finds that in section, portions of the grey matter appear to intermingle with white matter.

a considerable part in shaping the head. Firstly is protects the roof of the cranium and minimizes the effect of blows upon the upper surface of the head which without it might be fatal. It also gives attachment to some of the muscles which enable the dog to forcibly close its mouth and in this way it increases the power to bite and kill game.

In the smaller brachycephalic, short-faced dogs, such as the Pug, Pekingese and Griffon, the sagittal crest is poorly developed but the power to bite (and bite hard) is provided in these breeds mainly by the masseter muscle, which underlies the skin of the region of the cheeks. This muscle arises not so much from the sagittal crest as from the curved zygomatic arch. Although a Peke can give a powerful bite if it so desires, it would have little reason to use it in practice as it is very unlikely that a dog of this shape could run down a rabbit for example and certainly it would have insufficient length of jaw to kill it and devour it, even if it could catch it. This also points to the fact that the earlier specimens of brachycephalic dogs must have been scavengers and it is likely that they were the first to recognize the virtues and value of domesticity in submission to man.

Usually a well-developed sagittal crest extending from occiput above to the frontal sinuses below, will accompany a long, narrow head, with a rather straight, only slightly curved zygomatic arch, and long-jaws well armed with teeth capable of killing prey and tearing it to pieces.

The *temporal fossa* lies on either side of the sagittal crest. Although it is treated anatomically as being a cavity, the space in the living dog is (with the exception of the *coronoid process of the mandible* the lower jawbone) almost completely filled by the *temporal muscle*, the purpose of which is to close to the lower jaw, this being one of the muscles concerned in mastication of food.

The temporal muscle is attached to the sagittal crest and to the surface of the parietal bones and it is inserted below into the coronoid process of the mandible, in company with the masseter muscle, also a very powerful agent in the process of mastication. (*See Fig. 10*)

The *masseter muscle* completely fills the considerable depression

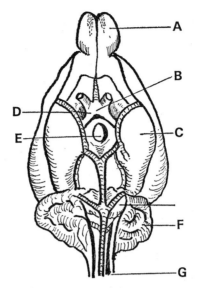

Fig. 8. The under surface of the brain
The striated lines represent the bloodvessels supplying the brain

A. *Olfactory bulb (Smell)*   D. *Optic Chiasma*   G. *Medulla oblongata*
B. *Optic chiasma (sight)*   E. *Hypophysis*
C. *Piriform lobe*   F. *Cerebellum*

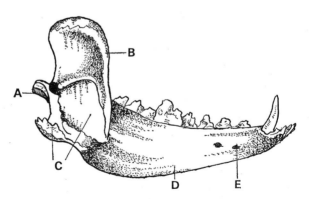

Fig. 9. Lower jaw of dog

A. *Condyle*   D. *Ramus*
B. *Coronoid process*   E. *Mental foramen*
C. *Area for muscle attachment*

lying immediately below the zygomatic arch and forms the foundation of the cheek, the skin of which covers the muscle. At its upper
portion it is attached to the zygoma and temporal bone and it is
attached below to the whole of the upright portion of the mandible
of the lower jaw. The upper end of the mandible, known as the
coronoid process, extends above the inner surface of the zygoma
and moves freely in the orbit above the eyeball. A well-developed
masseter produces large cheeks, as in the Bull terriers.

Both of these muscles, the temporal and masseter, are closely
associated and even somewhat interwoven.

Both muscles close the jaws by leverage upon the coronoid process while the temporal muscle serves also to keep the jaws closed
when the mouth is not functioning and acting as the channel
for the admission of food.

The temporal muscle is able to retract the lower jaw, and the
masseter to carry out side-to-side movements of the lower jaw. Those
breeds which require to hold on to living prey rather than kill
by a snap of the mouth, need strong masseter muscles which
necessitates the development of *cheeks*. Terriers and dogs which
snap at their prey and possibly shake it, make more use of their
temporal muscles except when serious chewing is the order of
the day. The masseter is then called into use. Such dogs tend to
shake and drop small prey rather than carry, just as a terrier snaps
up at a rat and shakes it to death.

Gundogs, on the other hand, carry relatively heavy game in
their mouths by use of the temporal muscles rather than the
masseter. This is in keeping with a " soft mouth ". The masseter
muscles, and accordingly the cheeks, are not usually developed
in spaniels and retrievers to the same extent as in dogs which fight
and depend upon being able to hang onto an adversary, or onto
heavy prey. These need the extra power provided by the masseter
and therefore many of them have marked cheek development,
while the spaniels and retrievers have less curved zygomas
and narrower skulls, and correspondingly less well-developed
cheeks.

The frontal bone of the dog extends from the suture at the
lower end of the parietal bone downwards to the upper ends of

the nasal bones centrally and to the superior maxillae (upper jaw bones) laterally. (*See Fig. 1*)

The frontal bone forms the inner casing of the orbit in which the eyeball rests.

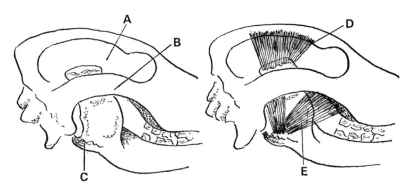

Fig. 10. Diagram showing muscles which open and close the mouth

A. Orbit
B. Zygoma
C. Coronoid process of mandible

D. Temporal muscle
E. Masseter muscle

The two muscles mainly concerned in opening and closing the mouth are the temporal muscle and the masseter muscle.

The powerful temporal muscle arises from the whole of the temporal fossa, on either side of the sagittal crest and overlying the temporal bones.

It is inserted in the upper end of the coronoid process of the maxilla but its fibres mingle here with those from the masseter muscle.

The action of the temporal muscle is to raise the lower jaw and also to retract it.

The masseter muscle, equally powerful, underlies the skin of the cheek while the temporal muscle underlies that of the forehead and helps to shape it.

The masseter arises from the lower

rim of the zygoma and is inserted below into the roughened surface of the coronoid process of the maxilla below the point of insertion of the temporal muscle, although as has been mentioned above their fibres may mingle.

The masseter muscle plays the principal part in closing the jaws and it also enables the jaw to be carried on one or other side by its unilateral contraction.

A third smaller muscle—the digastricus—lying immediately behind the upper part of the hinder edge of the mandible, aids in opening the mouth.

The above figures are purely diagrammatic and intended to show the points of attachment and direction of the muscle fibres.

As mentioned earlier, the dog has an *open orbit* but it can be seen from Fig. 3 that a small projection from the centre of the inner edge of the frontal bone lies opposite a similar projection on the inner edge of the zygoma. Between these two points stretches a thin ligamentous band which serves to maintain a separation between the temporal fossa above and the orbital fossa, and its contained eyeball, below.

Immediately above eye level on either side of the lower end of the forehead, there exists in most dogs, particularly in gundogs and hounds, a raised prominence which contains within it an air chamber. Between the two prominences there is usually a depression extending downwards to the upper level of the nasal bones, known as the " stop ". The degree of " stop " development varies in different breeds.

The air chamber contained within the frontal bone is known as the *frontal sinus*. The one on the one side of the head is separated from its fellow on the other side by a bony partition in most dogs, but not in all.

The hollow between the two sinuses, the *stop*, varies from a slight depression to a cavity into which one may press the bulb of one's finger tip, especially in the Pekingese.

The stop acts, too, as the medium by which the forehead is separated from the nasal passages.

The stop is regarded as a very important show point, either as regards its absence or its degree of development. In some breeds the exaggeration of this feature probably predisposes to other defects, mainly concerned with the palate. Cleft palates and very deep stops usually go together, especially in the short-faced breeds. Another complication accompanying the over-deep stop is a heavy ridge of skin transversely placed above the nostrils. This produces ridges and furrows which give rise to troublesome dermatitis, especially in Pekingese and Bulldogs.

The *frontal sinus* in the dog is of considerable extent in some of the larger breeds, especially in the hunting dogs which work by scent, but is rather less so in the running dogs which hunt by sight. It is variable in the short-faced dogs and although these have a very pronounced stop, the capacity of the frontal sinuses is usually limited in most of the brachycephalic breeds.

The sinuses communicate with the nasal passages by means of the *ethmoid meatus*. They also communicate with a second sinus situated in the maxillary bone underlying the cheek.

These *maxillary sinuses* lie within the bone just above the level of the cheek teeth and coincide in position with the last four of these. The roots of these teeth may lie within the sinuses or be separated from the actual chamber by a thin layer of bone. When one of the tooth roots becomes infected and an abscess develops, it invariably breaks onto the surface of the face immediately below the eye.

The purposes of these air chambers within the skull is mainly to add to the substance of the structure without producing too much additional weight. They provide sufficient width of face to permit the attachment of the upper jaw bones without interruption of the normal contour. It is wrong to suppose the sinuses play any very important part in respiration as they fill with air during expiration and not during inspiration. Moreover, they contain no nerve endings capable of conveying to the brain any impression of smell so, contrary to general opinion, they do not in any way influence the ability of the animal to recognize or analyse odours.

The *nasal bones* are small in the dog. Usually the upper ends are narrower than the lower but sometimes the contrary holds good. Their outer surfaces are often slightly concave, especially in the smaller breeds. Their lower ends, instead of being pointed or peaked as in the majority of animals, are notched or concave.

The *nasal cavity* is divided into two symmetrical halves in the longitudinal direction by a plate of cartilage known as the *septum nasi*.

The nasal chambers contain three passages through which air passes backwards to the larynx on its way to the lungs.

The passages arise from the presence within the nasal chambers of the *ethmoid bone* at its upper extremity, very much perforated in sieve-like manner, closely associated at its anterior end with the *upper and lower turbinated bones*.

These are thin plates of bone rolled upon themselves in scroll-like formation and covered with a highly vascular mucous membrane which also contains the nerve endings capable of appreciating odours.

The upper nasal passage passes between the upper turbinated bone and the lower surface of the nasal bones; the middle passes between the two turbinated bones, while the third lies between the lower turbinated bone and the floor of the skull, the palatine bones which carry the hard palate.

The *lower jawbone*, usually referred to as the *mandible*, or *inferior maxilla*, is practically straight from the incisor teeth back to its posterior angle, when it becomes erect. This upright portion is termed the *coronoid process*. (*See Figs. 6 and 9*) It articulates by means of the *condyle* with the *glenoid cavity* lodged in the temporal bone and underlying the upper end of the zygoma.

The coronoid process extends some way above this, entering the temporal fossa, and moving freely within it.

The two halves of the lower jaw, known as the *rami*, meet at their lower end half-way along the incisor teeth but except in very old dogs the two halves do not fuse together.

The outer aspect of the inferior maxilla is smooth apart from that of the coronoid process which is deeply recessed on the outer surface to receive the attachment of the masseter and temporal muscles.

The angle formed between the cranium and the remainder of the face lying below the stop, is referred to as the *cranio-facial angle*.

This angle varies in different breeds and although it is usually estimated by the judge's eye alone, accurate measurements have been recorded for most types of dogs.

Naturally the variation is not very marked but the matter of a few degrees of inclination produces considerable alteration in profile and the general appearance of the head. The degree is more marked in the " down-faced " breeds such as the Bull terriers. In other types the average angle between a line drawn down the forehead and another along the upper surface of the jaw is from twenty to twenty-five degrees.

The relative proportion existing between the cranial and facial divisions of the head are even more variable, with the cranial portion usually the longer. The precise relationship is commonly denoted in the standard of each breed.

For instant, in the Basenji:

"The distance from the top of the head to the stop is slightly more than from the stop to the tip of the nose."

In the Basset Hound:

"The top of the muzzle nearly parallel with a line from stop to occiput and not much longer than the head from stop to occiput."

In the Borzoi:

"Measurement equal from the occiput to the inner corner of the eye and from the inner corner to the tip of the nose."

In the Boxer:

"The length of the muzzle to the whole of the head should be as 1 is to 3."

The above will be sufficient to stress the need to study the standard of each particular breed.

As in the most carnivorous animals the *temporal fossae* of the dog are highly developed in comparison with those in other animals. The right and left halves in the larger breeds approach the mid-line in front, being separated higher up by the sagittal crest.

The *zygomatic arch* may be far more transversely curved in some breeds of dog than in the other domesticated animals.

In the Bulldog and related breeds, the transverse diameter between one zygoma and the other stands in relation to that of the long axis of the entire skull as 2 : 3, whereas in the horse it is 2 : 5.

The orbit faces almost centrally forward in most of the truly brachycephalic breeds while in the dolichocephalic (long-faced) breeds an imaginary line through the centre of each eyeball from front to rear, forms an angle approaching thirty degrees or more, with another line drawn longitudinally down the centre of the head and face.

In the brachycephalic heads such as those of the Pekingese, Pug and Bulldog, the cranium and zygoma are developed at the expense of the nasal bones and of those forming the base of the skull, notably the sphenoid and vomer bones, and sometimes the palatine plate of the upper jaw. (*See Fig. 5*)

This may result in faulty development of the hard palate and sometimes of the soft palate also (the latter more often in the Bulldog).

The *nasal chambers*, being so much shortened, may suffer from distortion of the turbinated bones which gives rise to difficulty in the passage of air between them with the result that the dog suffers from a persistent "snuffle" and may even attempt mouth-breathing to overcome its discomfort.

Cleft palate is not uncommon in short-faced puppies and even more so in strains in which the stop is deep and very pronounced. Although in these short-faced breeds the muscles which close the jaws may be well-developed, the jaws and teeth are so weak and ill-formed that none of these dogs, even if they had the speed, would be able to catch or kill, unaided, anything larger than a mouse. All of which leads one to believe that unless the efforts of mankind have wrought some drastic changes in these dogs over the course of time, the original brachycephalic dogs must have chosen domestication and been dependent upon human charity, or at least upon human companionship, ever since.

It is probable that cleft palate—which may sometimes be associated with hare-lip and even with umbilical hernia—is dependent upon genetic factors, or may be inherited as a simple Mendelian character. In litters of five or more, only two or three puppies may be affected but the apparently normal puppies may be carriers.

THE DENTITION OF THE DOG

Born toothless, the dog in later life comes into possession of twenty-eight *temporary teeth*, and eventually forty-two to forty-four *permanent teeth*. The temporary canines make their appearance at three to four weeks and all six should be in place by the fifth week. In Chihuahuas, Miniature Poms., and Yorkshires, as well as in the smaller brachycephalic breeds, it is not unusual for some of the incisors to be missing and this depends a good deal

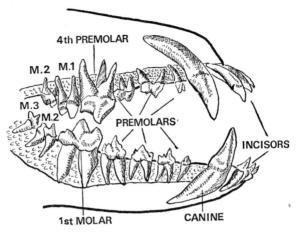

Fig. 11. Teeth of the adult dog

upon the width of the lower jaw. In Poodles, particularly Toys, efforts to increase the length of the muzzle have frequently resulted in narrow mouths, too small to contain the normal number of incisors. Conversely, Bulldogs and Boxers not unfrequently have seven or even more incisors above, below, or in both situations. This is regarded as a fault.

The permanent central and lateral incisors appear at four months while the temporary corner teeth are replaced by permanent teeth at four and a half to five months.

The canine teeth should be changed at about this time but not infrequently the temporary canines remain long after the permanent teeth are present.

The adult dog should own twelve incisors, four canines, sixteen premolars and ten molars. The teeth in the upper and lower jaws are not numerically equal.

The permanent dental formula for the dog is:

Incisors	Canines	Premolars	Molars
3	1	4	2
3	1	4	3

The lower jaw carries three molars against two in the upper jaw. The *Carnassial tooth*, the fourth premolar of the upper jaw is matched with the first molar of the lower, which it greatly resembles.

The first, second and third premolars appear at about three to four weeks and are changed between five and six months. Sometimes the first premolar, a small tooth, does not appear until the second month. At about the same time the first molar (the fifth cheek tooth) arrives in the upper jaw. The second molar should appear in the lower jaw at six to eight months but is frequently absent from the upper jaw.

The fact that certain breeds ranging from Poodles to Chihuahuas, have been systematically bred for show points with little regard for the state of the mouth, has resulted in the appearance of narrow jaws which cannot contain the prescribed number of teeth. As a result, teeth may be missing or displaced, or small teeth may appear in a double row. Absence of some of the promolars is common, and dogs lacking the required number may be disqualified in the show-ring. Nevertheless, one must remember that a few years ago in a number of prehistoric skulls unearthed, which had lain undiscovered many centuries before man took a hand in the dog business, defects prevailed similar to those which exist today. Moreover, there were gaps in the cheek teeth and a congenital absence of tooth sockets (alveoli), which would have made it impossible for the dog to own a full set of teeth.

Nevertheless, the prevailing belief is that absence of some of the premolars in long-headed breeds and of some of the premolars and even the carnassial teeth in the short-faced breeds, indicates a progressive hereditary weakness. More possibly it indicates a progressive tendency of breeders to pay more attention to outward appearance rather than to internal soundness.

THE SURFACE ANATOMY OF THE HEAD

From the knowledge now gained regarding the bony framework of the head, it should be comparatively easy, even with the eyes closed, to hold the dog's head between the thumb and fingers of

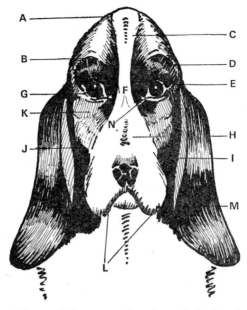

Fig. 12. The external surface of the head

A. *Occiput*
B. *Temporal muscle lying in temporal fossa*
C. *Sagittal crest*
D. *Frontal sinus*
E. *Orbit*

F. *Stop*
G. *Cornea of eyeball*
H. *Nasal bones*
I. *Superior maxilla*
J. *Cheek (masseter muscle)*

K. *Zygoma*
L. *Flews*
M. *Leather*
N. *Third eyelid*

the two hands and gently palpate and recognize all the bony features of the skull, as well as some of the more important muscles.

It is to be presumed that the dog is amiable, otherwise it would be safer to keep both eyes wide open.

Take the head gently in both hands while in front of the dog, or if the dog is not co-operative work from behind the head, allowing the hands to work gradually forwards.

Let the second and third fingers of each hand stray down the appropriate side of the head so that the two sides can be compared and felt simultaneously in order to provide a more accurate impression of the whole head.

Commence at the highest level of the forehead working from the base of one ear to that of the other.

The fingers will now be resting on the *occiput* and its size and degree of development can be estimated. In some breeds a prominent occiput is regarded as a virtue but in others it is said to be undesirable. In the gundogs it should be well developed. Some standards demand a skull flat or straight between the ears while others like it slightly domed.

Flat foreheads, between the ears, are expected in Toy Terriers, Basenjis, Italian Greyhounds, Cavaliers, Pekingese, Boston Terriers, Chow Chows, Collies, Dalmatians, French Bulldogs, Samoyeds, Corgis, Greyhounds and Whippets, to name a few breeds.

A prominent occiput is demanded in the Afghan, together with a prominent *dome* in the Basset Hound. The Bloodhound has a very prominent occiput and the Borzoi a slightly developed one. The skull is domed in the apple-headed Chihuahua, and in the Beagle, and slightly so in the Alsatian, while the Poodles carry a slight peak at the back.

The skull is slightly *rounded* between the ears in the Papillon and St. Bernard; slightly arched in the Dachshund and Boxer. It is more rounded in the Griffon; and in the Pug, without being apple-headed.

The *forehead* itself may be flat or rounded, narrow or wide. In the Boston Terrier the skull is square and flat on top while in the French Bulldog the forehead is domed and wrinkled. In the Great Dane the forehead is flat with a slight indentation running up its centre. That of the Shih Tzu is broad and round with width between the eyes but in the Tibetan Terrier the skull must not be broad or coarse, not domed, and absolutely flat between the ears. In the Corgi, while flat between the ears, the skull must taper towards the eyes and be slightly domed above them.

In the gundogs generally, the occiput is well marked and the skull domed but variations from this rule occur among the Retrievers, and the separate varieties of this family have several differences, not only as regards their breed but also they vary a good deal in type even in the same breed.

Running down from the centre of the forehead one may recognize the *sagittal crest*, more marked in some breeds than others. Excepting in the case of the smaller brachycephalic breeds most dogs have a sagittal crest but in many it is concealed from the touch by well-developed *temporal muscles* which are attached to it and may even bulge slightly above it. In the Irish Wolfhound and the Borzoi, the sagittal crest is well-marked and the heads long, so that the sagittal crest in these dogs actually plays some part in shaping the outline of the skull.

In the Chihuahua, the presence of the "*fontanelle*", the central gap between the cranial bones may usually be felt, even in the adult dog, or for that matter in the older one also. The Standard refers to the gap as "Molero". It lies at the junction of the two parietal bones with the frontal bone.

The orbit, the cavity surrounded by a bony circle, can be distinguished easily. By tracing this backward from the outer corner of the eye the zygoma can easily be felt, together with the zygomatic arch which juts out from the side of the cranium for a considerable distance in many breeds but may be close to and parallel with the cranium in others.

In a Bulldog or a Pekingese there will be room to insert the fingertips between the zygoma and the temporal muscle covering the cranium, while in a Fox terrier or a Whippet, this would probably be impossible.

On either side of the forehead, above and a little medial to each eyeball, is an elevation divided between the eyes by the upper part of the stop. This stop also separates the skull proper from the face. The two elevations are caused by the presence of underlying air cavities contained mainly within the frontal bone. These *frontal sinuses* vary in size in the different breeds and are particularly well-developed in the gundogs and hounds. They play a considerable part in shaping the head of a Cocker spaniel or a Beagle but not so much that of a Fox terrier or a Greyhound. In the short-faced breeds they are usually only slightly developed but this varies even in different individuals of the same breed.

The frontal sinuses, as such, are seldom mentioned in breed standards although occasional references are made to "*brows*". In the standard of the Deerhound one reads: "The head should be long, the skull rather flat then round with a very slight rise over the eyes, but nothing approaching a *stop*".

In the ordinary course of events the stop is accentuated when the frontal sinuses are extra large as occurs in most dogs which have wide nostrils and hunt by scent. As mentioned earlier, however, there is no direct relationship between the size of the frontal sinus and the ability to detect odours, other than that the additional width of forehead obtained through the presence of the sinuses enables the dog to carry a wider and more efficient nasal apparatus.

All the brachycephalic breeds such as the Pug and Pekingese, have deep stops owing to the small size of the nasal bones and the disparity between the development of the upper part of the skull and the foreface, together with the exaggerated size of the zygomatic arch. In these two breeds a transverse ridge of skin often separates the face from the short muzzle and the nose.

Feeling the cheeks with the fingers on either side of the face, one can readily pick out the *masseter muscle* arising from the lower edge of the *zygoma* and trace it back to the coronoid process of the lower jaw into which it is inserted.

By placing the tip of the second finger on the upper end of the zygoma and gently opening the mouth of the dog, one can feel the *articulation of the jaw,* and the *condyle* of the lower half gliding within the *glenoid fossa* as it lies beneath the highest portion of the zygoma.

The lower end of the *inferior maxilla* can be traced from the posterior angle of the jaw forward to the *chin* and *incisor teeth* and one can feel the meeting of the two *rami* directly below the *alveoli*—the sockets in the bone into which the incisor teeth fit.

Raising the upper and depressing the lower lip, will expose the *incisor teeth and the canines.* It will be noticed that there is only a small *interdental space*—the gap between the canine tooth and the first premolar.

It can now be determined whether the mouth is level, has a scissors bite, or if it is undershot, overshot or just right. The number of each kind of tooth may be checked to see if they are all present, and also if they are in line, or crowded and overlapping. In some puppies and young dogs there may be a double set of incisor teeth, the one piled up behind the others; or there may be fewer than the approved number. By gently opening the mouth,

D

or by drawing back the lips, the premolars and molars can be seen, counted and examined to ascertain whether all are present.

The *ears* can be inspected and the flaps or *leathers* palpated. It can also be ascertained whether the formation of the ear flap corresponds with the type, position and size required by the breed standard.

The *eyes* can be inspected for colour of the *iris*, whether light, dark or wholly or partly devoid of pigment. The *cornea*—the window of the eye—should be glass-clear and bright, reflecting the light. On the other hand it may be dull, partly opaque, or dotted or streaked with opacities, or pitted by an ulcer.

The *eyelids* may be examined and it will be noted if they are wide open, normally shaped, or turned inwards (entropion), or outwards (ectropion). In some breeds c.f., Toy white poodles, the eyelids should carry a rim of black pigment.

The *nostrils* will be inspected to ascertain whether they are black, pink or liver-coloured, and whether or not they carry white markings.

The general shape of the head, the shape of the forehead and the dome, the degree of development of the sagittal crest and of the frontal sinuses, the state of the occiput and the degree of curvature of the zygomatic arch, the length, width and depth of the muzzle, can all be observed with ease in a short, smooth-coated breed, but in the case of the long-coated breeds ranging from Old English Sheepdogs to Pekingese and Poodles, the hair may be parted with the finger tips. Much more accurate information can be gained if one knows something of the underlying bonework and has a well-developed sense of touch.

THE EAR

The ear may be considered in three parts, (a) the ear flap or *external ear* (b) the *middle ear*, which includes the *ear canal*, and the *tympanum* or *ear drum* and its surrounding cavity (c) the very complicated structures associated with the internal ear, concerned not only with hearing but also with gravity, balance and the proprioceptive sense, which relates the position of the body to surrounding objects and to its place in space.

There is no animal or species, probably, which exhibits so many variations in ear shape and ear carriage as the domestic dog. This applies to many features other than ears, for man has evolved from the dog's original ancestors hundreds of varieties, of which no two are really alike while others are so dissimilar as to be almost unrecognizable as members of the same species.

Many of these ear variations arise from the reduction in size of a breed, or from breeding down from a larger original variety or strain without a corresponding shrinkage in the size of the skin in the smaller, resulting specimen.

In order to absorb some of the surplus the normal erect ears, as seen in the wolf, become converted into large skin flaps as happens in the spaniels and hounds. It will usually be found that any dog with long, pendulous ear flaps—the bloodhound for example—will have an immense amount of loose skin covering its body. To emphasize this the skin at the scruff of the neck can be lifted in this breed for a foot into the air before one begins to feel the weight of the dog.

It is true that large ear flaps are sometimes present in varieties which have not undergone any marked reduction in size but these are considerably smaller than the ears of one that has done so.

Another of nature's methods of taking up an excess of skin is by the formation of a dewlap and this may often be seen in company with large, pendulous ear flaps. Yet another method, seen usually in the skin of the forehead and face as well as on the limbs, is the development of skin folds and wrinkles.

Most of the smaller varieties of ears, especially those which are moulded by the shapes of the ear cartilages into *rose ears* as in the greyhound, and whippet; and again in the Italian greyhound; are found in dogs without a great excess of skin. An exception is seen in the Bulldog, which has rose ears and a lot of skin but this is taken up largely by a dewlap and a great deal of wrinkling, especially around the neck and face.

These rose ears fold inwards at their rear portion, while their upper, front edges curve outwards and backwards, exposing part

of the inside of the " burr ", which is also produced by a characteristic wrinkling of the ear cartilage.

Erect ears are associated with a fairly close-fitting skin in most
instances. Any excess or undue thickening of the skin, particularly
in the neck region, will often result in drooping of the ears, as
is seen not infrequently in coarse, heavy-skinned types of Alsatian.

Many kinds of ear shape and carriage have turned up as
mutations and have been encouraged by breeders until they have
become fixed characteristics.

For the purpose of studying the external ear and its structure,
we will take as an example the erect ear of the Alsatian, which
contains the same structures as are found in every other type of
ear but in more simple form.

The External Ear

This is built up by the introduction of three central cartilages,
covered externally by normal skin, growing hair, and internally by
a modified skin containing few hair follicles but a great many
sebaceous glands, some of which secrete a waxy material.

In certain breeds, notably Poodles, the tendency to grow hair
well down into the ear canal appears to be increasing, with undesirable consequences.

The many bloodvessels and nerves entering the ear, pass between
skin and cartilage mostly on the outer but also on the inner surfaces
of the ear. The nerves and bloodvessels travel in company and
have two separate sources. Those supplying the middle, and hinder
surfaces of the outer ear pass beneath the parotid gland to the base
of the ear.

Those supplying the front edge of the outer surface of the ear
as well as the under surface, enter the ear at the level of the zygoma.

The muscles which control the ear movements lie beneath the skin
of the outer surface of the ear flap. They are attached to the surface
of the cartilages at one end and to the zygoma, frontal bone,
occipital bone and structures in the neck region, at the other
end.

There are in all fifteen muscles operating each ear but as some of these are multiple, the number can be increased to nineteen. Some erect and adduct (bring closer together) the ears; others depress and usually adbuct them (farther apart). Others rotate them in the direction better to catch sounds.

The *main or conchal cartilage* of the ear takes the shape of the flap but may best be described as being trumpet-shaped. The skin covering its outer side carries hair and is thicker than that on its inner surface which is usually hairless or comparatively so. In Cocker spaniels, fifty years ago, the inner surface carried hair in order to protect the skin against thorns and brambles. Nowadays the inner surface is usually hairless except at the edges. In some breeds, especially in Poodles, hair may grow some way down the skin of the ear canal. The cast-off hairs cannot escape and set up ear irritation.

The ear cartilage is attached around its base to a ring-shaped *annular cartilage* which is adherent at its lower end to the bony external orifice of the ear canal situated on the surface of the cranium.

A third cartilage—*the scutular cartilage*—a small plate of irregular outline, lies upon the temporal muscle in front of the base of the main conchal cartilage.

The ear is held erect partly by muscular action and also to a variable extent in different individuals, by the skin of the neck region which draws the tip of the ear upwards when it contracts.

The scutular cartilage, lying beneath the skin on the surface of the forehead, is the smallest cartilage of the three, but is very important as a number of muscles are attached to it and it has to have its own position fixed by the action of other muscles arising from the zygoma and frontal bones, before it can operate.

The ears of an Alsatian puppy, as in many other breeds normally possessing erect ears, may be quite upright while the body carries puppy fat, with the skin of the neck held firmly, say at three months of age, but between four and five months the ears may droop or

fall sideways or forward upon the head. In most cases by the time
the puppy reaches six months the ears should again become erect
and it is to be hoped they will stay this way.

In Collies the ears should be erect when the dog's attention is
engaged, with the tips pendulant when the dog is listening. During
repose the ears are folded back.

The differences between the ears of each breed are carefully
recorded in the various standards and as they are so numerous
and detailed they should be studied in each standard and then in
specimens of the individual breeds.

The *ear canal* or *meatus* is lined by skin and is subject to the
usual disorders affecting skin.

It is irregular in its lumen at the outer end, being broken up
by the shape of the underlying ear cartilage. Its middle third is
directed downwards and has a smooth lining. After travelling in
this direction for an inch or more according to breed and size of the
dog, the canal turns at right angles towards the middle of the head,
and is cut off from the *internal ear* by the thin, translucent *tympanum* or *ear drum*. Beyond this point the internal ear consists
of a narrow chamber within the temporal bone containing air, and
contains three small bones, the *malleus* (hammer), the *incus* (anvil)
and the *stapes* (stirrup). These bones are hinged and move in
relation to the vibrations set up in the tympanum by sound waves.
The vibrations are transmitted to the nervous mechanism of the
bony labyrinth within the temporal bone. Contained within the
internal ear are also the semi-circular canals which are concerned
with body balance.

THE MOUTH

The mouth extends from the lips to the pharynx, which is a
membranous pouch reaching from the articulation of the two
jawbones back as far as the opening into the oesophagus (gullet or
food pipe).

The mouth is divided into two parts (a) the *vestibule*, the space
between the inner sides of the lips and cheeks and the teeth. (b)

the *mouth cavity*, contained within the dental arches and gums. This is bounded above by the hard and soft palates, while the mouth floor is formed by the tongue and by its surrounding tissues which bind the tongue to the lower jaw.

The Lips

The outer surfaces of the lips are covered with hair in most breeds apart from a small triangular space on the middle of each upper lip.

The hairs are of two kinds, (a) fine and (b) long, rather stiff *tactile hairs*, more numerous on the upper lip and the central area beneath the lower lip. These hairs convey sensation to the skin and this is recorded by the brain. The lips contain muscular tissue and glands. The inner surface of each lip is lined by mucous membrane continuous with that of the mouth. In the mid line of the mouth the mucous membrane develops a small fold which attaches lip to gum and this is known as the *fraenum of the lip*.

At the margins of the lip, skin meets mucous membrane.

The inner surface of each cheek is pierced at the level of the carnassial tooth by the parotid duct which conveys saliva into the mouth.

The submaxillary glands discharge their saliva through a small opening on either side of the fraenum of the tongue.

The Hard Palate

The hardness of the structure depends upon the presence of a thick, dense and corrugated mucous membrane attached to the periosteum of the bones forming the roof of the mouth. These are the palatine, maxillary and premaxillary.

The roof of the mouth is imperfectly divided into two halves by a median, longitudinal raphe. Each half of the mucous membrane is raised into nine to ten curved transverse folds, each with its convexity looking forwards.

The Soft Palate

This structure forms a rather extensive, movable partition between the mouth and the pharynx. It is attached in front to the bony palate with its hinder edge free and in contact with the epiglottis, which is the opening into the larynx capable of being covered over by the soft palate whenever food passes above the epiglottis on its way into the oesophagus.

The Tonsils

These lie on either side of the pharynx immediately behind the root of the tongue and they can be viewed in the living dog if the mouth is widely opened and the base of the tongue gently depressed. They are masses of lymphoid tissue designed to trap bacteria.

The Pharynx

This tubular structure lying behind the tongue, is concerned with the passage of air into the trachea via the larynx as well as with the passage of food into the stomach via the oesophagus.

In front it communicates with both nasal passages and the mouth, separating the one from the other whenever the soft palate is caused to descend.

The upper part of the pharynx is therefore concerned mainly with breathing while the lower part is concerned with deglutition (the act of swallowing), though between meals or when saliva is being swallowed the whole of the pharynx may take part in the act of breathing. Dogs are mainly nose breathers though the mouth may play a part during rapid exercise or even on a very hot day.

Suffocation arising from swelling of the soft palate with consequent closure of the pharynx, or with accompanying closure of the laryngeal opening, is by no means unknown, especially during hot weather, and this is particularly common in the short-faced varieties such as the Bulldog.

Into the upper part of the pharynx the Eustachian tubes enter. These are two paired channels which open at their upper extremity into the middle ear in order to permit a column of air to support the inner surface of the tympanum of the ear. Without the Eustachian tubes—or when through infection they become swollen and blocked—a partial vacuum is created in the middle ear and the tympanic membrane is sucked inwards, becoming concave instead of flat. This causes temporary deafness and is the reason for deafness accompanying the common cold.

The Tongue

As the dog seldom chews its food except in an effort to reduce a chunk of meat into portions capable of being swallowed whole, the tongue does not have a lot of manipulation required of it, other than to divert unmasticated food into the gullet.

The tongue is composed mainly of muscular tissue covered by mucous membrane. Its anterior end is thin and spatulate while the hinder part is thick and triangular in section.

The dorsum of the tongue, the portion applied to the roof of the mouth, is divided longitudinally (like the roof) into two portions joined together, but distinguished by the presence of a longitudinal groove which separates the muscles into two symmetrical groups, one on either side of the tongue. At its hinder part the dorsum of the tongue carries from four to six small raised circles, the *circumvallate papillae,* which are concerned with taste.

The root of the tongue is attached to the *hyoid bone* as well as to the lower jaw. Beneath its free terminal portion a double fold of mucous membrane—the *fraenum linguae*—unites the under surface of the tongue to the floor of the mouth.

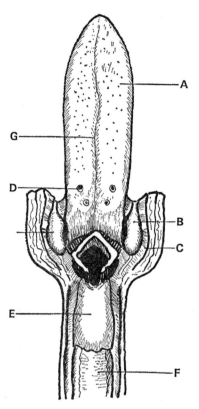

Fig. 13. The Tongue, Pharynx and Larynx

A. Tongue
B. Tonsil
C. Epiglottis—a laryngeal
   cartilage

D. Circumvallate papillae
E. Pharynx
F. Oesophagus
G. Sulcus

The tongue of the dog is thin when compared with that of most other domesticated animals, other than the cat. It is long and spatulate in shape and extremely motile, being able to turn in any direction. This applies only to the anterior, free portion, about two-thirds of the whole length.

The hinder part of the tongue is thicker and triangular in section with the base uppermost. The extreme hinder portion, known as the dorsum, lies when at rest in contact with both the soft and hard palates. The root of the tongue situated behind the tongue's body, is attached to the hyoid bone and to the inner aspect of the mandible.

The dorsum of the tongue is divided into two longitudinal halves by a groove—the sulcus—shallow near the tip and deeper at the rear end.

The Hyoid Bone

This bone supports the tongue and pharynx. It is made up of three parts joined together. The middle portion, the *body of the bone* is short and carries the central portion anteriorly which is buried in the tissues at the root of the tongue. The upper portion is by far the greater and consists of a long strap-shaped piece of bone situated one on each side of the mouth, passing upwards along the inside of the pharynx beneath its mucous membrane. It is anchored at its upper end to the underside of the cranium. The hinder end of the body of the hyoid passes on either side of the arytenoid cartilage immediately below the epiglottis and is finally attached to the thyroid cartilage of the larynx. (*See Fig. 17*)

The larynx and oesophagus are discussed on pages 72 to 74.

The whole of the mucous membrane covering the dorsum is studded with elevations known as lingual papillae, of which there are five varieties present in every tongue, each occupying a definite position.

The under surface of the tongue is smooth and is attached by a median fold to the mucous membrane of the floor of the mouth. This fold is known as the fraenulum. Other folds of mucous membrane connect the tongue to the soft palate and the epiglottis. When a dog swallows, the movement of the tongue pulls the epiglottis down over the opening into the larynx, and the food passes above the closed epiglottis into the pharynx and thence down the oesophagus. If the epiglottis failed to close in this way, the dog would inhale food into the trachea and then into the lungs.

The Pharynx

This is a muscular membranous tube extending from the rear of the mouth as far back as the joint between the first and second neck bones. The dog breathes through the pharynx as well as using it for the passage of food. In the dorsal part of the pharynx the air passage through the nostrils opens and on either side of the pharynx there is an opening through which the Eustachian tube enters. The Eustachian tube connects the middle ear with the pharynx and thus permits inspired air to come into contact with the inner aspect of the tympanum or ear drum.

Unless the pressure on both sides of the tympanum were balanced in this way by means of an open, healthy Eustachian tube, deafness would result.

THE EYE

A full description of the eye would require a volume of its own, so we will discuss only its main features with special reference to the retina which may be the seat of hereditary disease and to the outer surface of the eye—the cornea and sclera—which are particularly exposed to injury.

The Eyelids

There are two main eyelids in the dog, an upper and a lower, together with a third eyelid known as the *membrana nictitans*, which lies largely hidden between the upper and lower lids in the inner corner of the eye.

The third eyelid, playing the part of a windscreen wiper, flicks across the outer surface of the front of the eyeball whenever the cornea is accidentally touched or threatened, and also whenever slight pressure is placed upon the eye through the partly closed lids.

Behind the eyeball there is a pad of soft fat which acts as a buffer and shields the eye from injury when struck.

But, in addition, it holds the eye firmly against the inner surface of the lids especially when the animal is in good condition and the fat behind the eyeball plentiful.

In thin, emaciated dogs the fat tends to disappear behind the eyeball and so the eye " falls back into the head " permitting the two main eyelids to partially close over the eye. All this throws the tear ducts out of position and so the membrana nictitans protrudes over the eyes which weep tears that scald the lids and produce sores around and below the eyes.

The pad of fat at the back of the eye is attached to the membrana nictitans and when the eye retracts within the orbit through the pull of the retractor muscle lying behind the eyeball, the fat is depressed into the orbit and causes the membrana nictitans to travel upwards across the eye. This third eyelid is also useful as it distributes tears over the surface of the cornea and keeps it moist, as well as removing dust particles, insects and other offending bodies. The eyelids are lined by a smooth, sensitive and moist membrane, the *conjunctiva*, which is continuous over the front of the eyeball.

Of the two main eyelids the upper does most of the work of opening and closing the eye, the lower remaining almost passive. Their reflexes, particularly those of the upper lid, are very fast so that actual lid movements may be almost invisible.

Occasionally, especially in some strains of Poodles and in short-faced dogs possessing prominent eyes, there may be some interference with the passage of tears down the tear ducts into the nose so that there is an almost constant passage of tears from the nasal corner (canthus) of the eye down over the face. In addition, especially in dogs carrying an excess of body skin, the eyelids, more often the lower, may roll inwards so that the outer surface of the lower eyelid, together with any short hairs it may carry, will cause friction upon the underlying cornea with soreness and possibly ulceration. This is the condition known as *entropion*.

The Eyeball

In the dog the eyeball is not a perfect sphere as it measures rather more from front to back than either transversely or vertically. (*See Fig. 14*)

This is due partly to the fact that the *cornea*, the transparent part of the eye, which is set into the white *sclera*, the wall of the eyeball, like a watch glass, bulges slightly since the diameter of the cornea is less than that of the sclera.

The cornea is not only transparent allowing the passage of light into the interior of the eye, but it is of a homogeneous nature, thick and resistant and completely devoid of bloodvessels. The cornea is also thicker in its central portion than at its edges, a fact which adds to its "bulge". In shape it is not completely circular but is

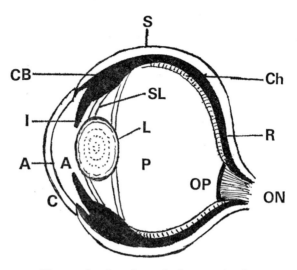

Fig. 14. Section through the eye of a dog

A. *Anterior chamber con-*   I. *Iris*   R. *Retina*
    taining aqueous fluid   L. *Lens*   S. *Sclera*
C. *Cornea*   ON. *Optic nerve*   SL. *Suspensory ligament*
CB. *Ciliary body*   OP. *Optic papilla—the*   *of lens*
Ch. *Choroid*   *" blind spot "*   P. *Posterior chamber*

Lying beneath the retina but not shown in the diagram is the tapetum cellulosum. This is a layer of iridescent cells superimposed on the choroid and lying directly behind the retina. Their purpose is to play the part of a mirror and reflect some of the light passing into the eye back through th retina, thus increasing the intensity of the visual image. It is this layer which reflects back the lights of a car when they shine into a dog's eyes and it is also the cause of the glow observable in the eyes of a dog developing the primary " night blindness " phase of progressive retinal atrophy. As the pupils of the eyes become very dilated at this stage, the reflection from the tapetum becomes more obvious.

a little wider transversely, somewhat lozenge-shaped. It is extremely sensitive to touch.

The *sclera*—the " white of the eye ", is a dense, somewhat elastic and very tough white casing of considerable thickness, more especially behind it, where the optic nerve from the brain enters its wall and penetrates it, spreading out inside the eye to form the retina.

The sclera is also thicker around the margin which houses the cornea.

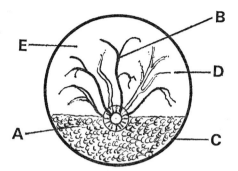

Fig. 15. The Retina and Tapetum and the fundus of the eye

As viewed through an ophthalmoscope.

Note the large branching bloodvessels emerging from the rounded optic disc.

The tapetum lucidum may be any shade of green, blue, orange red, chocolate, black or slatey-grey. The tapetum nigrum is chocolate or black but white in the albino.

The blood-vessels appear bright red.

In progressive retinal atrophy the blood vessels at first appear shortened and lighter in colour and finally almost disappear. The retina is therefore deprived of nutrition and ceases to function as a mirror reproducing its picture.

A. *Optic disc*
B. *Retinal bloodvessels*
C. *Tapetum (chocolate or black)*

D. *Tapetum yellow or green*
E. *Tapetum green*

In the normal eye of the dog, looking straight ahead through its eyelids, very little of the sclera is visible although it constitutes about three-quarters of the casing of the eyeball. The parts of the eye visible from the front are the cornea, with the underlying pigmented iris (the movable diaphragm) and a small pinkish nodule situated in the nasal canthus or corner, known as the *caruncle*, together with the three overlying eyelids.

The whole of the globe of the eyeball situated behind the cornea, comprises three layers:

(a) the outer *sclera* which is lined by (b) the choroid coat, a black layer, lined in turn by (c) the retina, which as previously stated is a thin layer derived from the spreading layers of the optic nerve. This membrane, the photographic film of the eye, fits accurately into the concavity within the choroid coat but is actually attached to it only at the spot where the optic nerve penetrates it (the *optic papilla* or the "blind spot") of the eye, and again at its anterior margin encircling the inside of the eyeball a little behind the corneal margin. The retina may become detached from the underlying choroid coat by a blow on the eyeball, or by an out-pouring of blood or exudate from the choroid coat.

The optic nerve penetrates the sclera a little below and slightly laterally to the centre of the eyeball.

Through its centre the bloodvessels supplying the retina penetrate and on entering the eyeball they take on an appearance reminiscent of miniature tree trunks giving off branches after a fairly definite pattern. These vessels are clearly visible when the interior of the eye is viewed through an electric ophthalmoscope.

In cases of progressive retinal atrophy the finer branches first disappear and then the larger branches, usually leaving behind black or brownish spots on a greyish background.

At the back of the dog's eye, within the choroid and behind the retina are several superimposed layers of glistening cells. These cause the eye to reflect light and glisten when the eye is viewed directly in such a position that bright light enters the eye. This is particularly the case when at night a motor headlamp shines into a dog's eyes. These layers collectively comprise what is known as the *tapetum*.

In early cases of retinal atrophy in which the pupil of the eye is dilated, and the tapetum becomes greenish in colour, this appearance may be visible in daylight, and it is closely associated with the phase of "night blindness" seen during the initial stages of this hereditary eye disease. The changes in the eye are progressive and usually continuous but the rate of development varies, ranging from weeks to years between the early appearance of night blindness and the onset of complete blindness.

The Iris and Uveal Tract

Continuous with the choroid coat and immediately surrounding the circumference of the cornea just behind the corneal margin, lies a ring of pigmented tissue, black and somewhat porous, known as the ciliary body. Together with the iris with which the ciliary body is continuous, the whole structure is referred to as the *uveal tract*.

The *iris* is a circular curtain, perforated by a rounded space the *pupil*, which becomes smaller when exposed to light, and dilates when it is dark. In young puppies the iris is usually blue, turning later to a dark chocolate shade, or it may be amber or brown.

The ciliary body secretes the *aqueous humour*, a saline solution which fills the *anterior chamber of the eye* and keeps the eyeball in its rounded shape. The *posterior chamber*, lying behind the lens, is filled with a soft jelly-like substance known as the *vitreous humour*. This permits the passage of light, keeps the retina in place and helps to support the lens from behind.

The pressure within the eyeball is controlled by the relationship between the rate of secretion of aqueous humour and its absorption into the lymphatic channels within the eyeball.

Fortunately in the dog the arrangement and adequacy of these channels is such that true primary glaucoma—a disease resulting from excessive pressure of fluid within the eyeball—is extremely rare.

Movements of the eyeball, somewhat limited in the dog which prefers to move its head and neck rather than its eyeball, are controlled by muscles attached to the outer surface of the sclera close behind the cornael margin, and at their other end to the bone of the skull surrounding the optic foramen, the aperture in the skull through which the optic nerve passes when leaving the cranium. These muscles also provide a protecting sheath which encloses the optic nerve between brain and eyeball.

E

CHAPTER TWO

THE NECK

IN many respects the neck of the dog may be a very variable quantity.

Its length, whether long and visible, or short and huddled into the dog's shoulders, depends upon the relative length of each of the seven vertebrae it contains, as well as upon the thickness of the intervertebral discs lying between adjacent vertebrae. Each of these consists of a cartilaginous fibrous portion forming the peripheral part of the disc, with a much softer central part (the nucleus pulposus). In cases of the so-called " slipped disc ", whether in the neck or some other portion of the spine, this soft centre becomes squeezed out and if it protrudes at the upper part of the disc it causes pressure upon the spinal cord as it passes between the two vertebrae, normally united by its aid. This gives rise to pain and symptoms of paralysis.

Intervertebral discs vary in thickness in different members of the same species and according to the animal's age. They are usually thicker in young animals and become thinner as they grow older. In older subjects they may become impregnated with calcium salts and produce fusion (anchylosis) of adjacent vertebrae.

The apparent length of the neck depends very considerably upon the degree of inclination of the scapula, whether it is sloping back at its upper end, or lying more perpendicularly.

An upright scapula appears not only to shorten the neck but in addition it influences the angle at which the neck is carried and also that of the head in relation to the neck.

One seldom encounters in the long-headed breeds a long neck in company with an upright shoulder, nor is it usual to find a sloping shoulder accompanied by a short neck.

In the short-faced (brachycephalic) breeds such as the Pug and Pekingese, the neck is short owing to corresponding shortness of each of the neck bones. In spite of the shortness of the neck in such breeds, the standard demands that the scapula should be inclined and not upright. The easy way to determine the degree of scapula inclination is to place one finger on the centre of the upper edge of the scapula and a finger of the other hand on the shoulder joint at the lower end of the scapula. An imaginary, or even a chalked line joining the two points will enable one to estimate the angle existing between the scapula and the ground upon which the dog stands, or alternatively one can measure the angle between the posterior edge of the scapula and the shaft of the humerus. The latter varies from eighty degrees in a well-inclined shoulder to 105 degrees in an upright shoulder. In the former case the inclination of a good shoulder may be approximately forty-five degrees or less while that of a bad, upright shoulder may be sixty to seventy degrees.

One of the difficult aspects of dog breeding results from the fact that a long neck is frequently expected to accompany a short back. In other words, the dorsal and lumbar vertebrae are expected to be short while the cervical vertebrae must in the same individual be relatively lengthy. That such a combination can be bred with a reasonable degree of consistency indicates that the length of the separate components of the spine, viz. the cervical, dorsal, lumbar bones and the sacrum may depend upon individual, genetic control, in much the same way that leg length is controlled in certain breeds. Were it otherwise the giraffe could never have come into existence.

The Cervical Vertebrae

Like other domesticated mammals the dog has seven neck bones. The first, articulating with the hinder end of the skull, is the *Atlas*. Following this is the *Axis*.

The *Atlas* is narrow from before to behind and its upper surface is curved but differs from the other neck bones in carrying no dorsal spine. The wings of the bone are wide and lie almost horizontally. Its articular surface is convex in front where it meets the rear end of the skull and concave behind in order that it may receive the odontoid process of the axis.

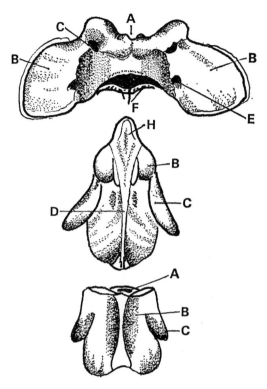

Fig. 16. The first three cervical vertebrae

1. The atlas—*from above*   *F. Neural canal*   *D. Neural spine*
A. The ring   *2. The axis*   *3.* Third cervical bone
B. Wing of atlas   *H. Odontoid process* *A. Neural Canal*
C. Antero-inferior fora-   *B. Articular process at its* *B. Body of bone*
  men   *base*   *C. Transverse process*
E. Posterior foramen   *C. Transverse process*

The wings of the atlas can be felt through the skin of the neck on either side immediately behind the occiput.

The *Axis* has at its anterior extremity a peak-like conical odontoid process which fits into the rear end of the atlas. It carries an articular facet on either side of the process.

The axis is remarkable in that it carries a relatively enormous neural spine on its upper surface, which distinguishes it at a glance from all the other vertebrae.

Attached along the upper edge of the neural spine of the axis is a flattened elastic cord known as the *ligamentum nuchae*. This ligament extends down the whole length of the neck as far as the dog's withers where it is attached to the tip of the spinous process of the first dorsal vertebra. It there becomes continuous with the *supraspinal* ligament which runs down the spine as far as the sacrum, being attached to each of the spinous processes.

The *ligamentum nuchae* helps to support the head and neck and also to effect a downward curvature of the cervical vertebrae. A short ligamentum nuchae helps to maintain high head carriage with the assistance of the very many muscles contained within the neck.

The remaining five neck bones follow the general pattern of the other bones of the spine since they carry spinous processes above and transverse and oblique processes laterally.

The transverse processes give attachment to the muscles of the neck while the oblique processes carry flat articular surfaces in front and behind each bone which articulate with similar surfaces on adjoining vertebrae.

A channel, the *neural canal*, traverses each vertebra longitudinally and through this the spinal cord passes from the medulla of the brain as far back as the last lumbar bone at its junction with the sacrum. On its way down the neck and back the spinal cord gives off nerves to all parts of the body. These leave the spine by passing through a space between the bodies of adjoining vertebrae.

Between the bodies of each pair of spinal bones in the neck and throughout the spine in general, there lies a cartilaginous *spinal disc* which helps to lessen concussion between the bones.

The neck is supported and moved in every direction by muscles passing between the transverse processes of the vertebrae and by others running the whole length of the neck. Some of these extend into the fore limb and help to move it and bring the limb forward, especially when head and neck are extended at the time (as during galloping).

One of these long muscles of the neck, known as the *brachiocephalic muscle*, commences at its attachment to the occipital bone of the skull and the anterior end of the ligamentum nuchae and at its other end is inserted into the humerus (armbone).

It will be evident from this that a strong, lengthy and well-developed neck considerably assists forward movement of the fore limb.

This important muscle has other uses also. When the fore limb is fixed and the muscle on one side contracts, the head and neck are turned in that direction.

The cervical bones do not run straight down the neck but curve downwards in their lower third and then run horizontally to meet the first dorsal bone between the two scapulae (bladebones).

The course of the bones can be felt with the fingers.

The neck, from the exhibition standpoint, is a very important part of the body, particularly as regards its length, the way in which it is carried and also as regards the way it joins into the body between the bladebones or scapulae.

If the scapulae, one on either side, are inclined from below upwards towards the rear end of the body, more of the lower end of the neck is exposed. When the two scapulae are placed in the body almost perpendicularly their front edges will extend forwards over the last cervical and sometimes over the sixth vertebra, and this will make the neck seem short. The junction between neck and body will then appear to be abrupt rather than level and stream-lined, and the neck will then probably appear to be set on almost perpendicularly instead of sloping gently upward towards the head, as it should do.

In the long-headed (dolichocephalic) varieties the neck should almost invariably be—or appear to be—lengthy, but in the short-faced breeds (brachycephalic) and in certain Toy breeds such as the Pomeranian, it is usual for the neck to appear rather shorter, but in spite of this standards demand that the shoulder blades should be well-inclined.

In the Papillon, Griffon and Chihuahua, the neck is of medium length with well sloped shoulders. In the Pinscher family the neck must be rather longer, strong but lean, graceful, slightly arched and without sign of throatiness.

In the Italian Greyhound the neck is long and gracefully arched

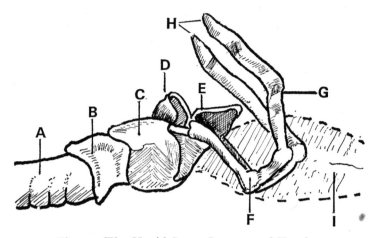

Fig. 17. The Hyoid Bone, Larynx and Trachea

A. *Trachea*
B. *Cricoid cartilage*
C. *Thyroid cartilage*
D. *Arytenoid cartilage*
E. *Epiglottis*
F. *Body of hyoid*

G. *Great cornua of hyoid bone*
H. *Attachment site of hyoid bone to petrous temporal bone of skull*
I. *Tongue*

and is usually somewhat erect with the head set with forehead and foreface closely approaching the horizontal when at rest.

The Larynx

This is a tubular organ made up of three paired and three single cartilages.

The paired cartilages are the *arytenoid, corniculate* and *cuneiform*, while the single are the *cricoid, thyroid* and the *epiglottis*.

The whole of these are articulated together to form a cartilaginous tube through which air passes from the nasal passages and less often through the mouth to travel down the trachea and into the lungs.

The largest of these cartilages is the thyroid which covers the front and sides of the larynx like a shield. The body of the thyroid carries a prominence known in ourselves as the " Adam's apple ", which can be felt at the upper part of the larynx in the centre line of the throat.

The larynx is suspended to the base of the skull through the hyoid bone which lies within and supports the tongue. The hyoid bone is connected to the upper surface of the thyroid cartilage by means of various ligaments.

The cricoid cartilage lies behind (or below) the thyroid cartilage and is shaped like a signet ring with the signet at its rear.

Resting on the upper border of the cricoid cartilage are the two wing-like arytenoid cartilages which open and close in some degree during respiration by the use of their attached muscles. In their interior and at their bases the arytenoid cartilages carry the vocal cords which produce various sounds according to the nature of their vibrations.

The epiglottis, a single cartilage, is four-sided and elastic in nature. It is connected with the thyroid cartilage by a narrow stem. Its anterior triangular portion is moved freely in an up-and-down direction by the use of muscles and it closes down upon the *glottis* (the opening from the pharynx into the centre of the larynx) whenever the dog swallows food or liquids, thus preventing either of them from being sucked into the lungs.

The lower border of the cricoid cartilage is connected by ligament to the first ring of the trachea.

The mucous membrane lining the larynx is continuous with that lining the pharynx and is also continuous with that of the trachea, which passes down the front of the neck to the lungs. It can be distinctly felt through the skin.

The trachea is made up of a series of rings, adjoining ones being held together by a ligament.

There are from thirty-five to forty of these in the dog. Each ring is slightly incomplete and the breaches lie in line down the upper (dorsal) part of the trachea.

Inside the thorax the trachea divides up within each lung into tubules much after the manner of the branching of a tree, including its lesser and minute twigs.

The Oesophagus

This tube, also referred to as the gullet or food-pipe, enters the chest by passing between the first pair of ribs slightly to the left of the trachea. It then moves over slightly to the right as it crosses the left bronchus (the first main division of the trachea). Within the chest it passes between and is supported by the two layers of the mediastinum, a thick membrane which lies centrally, dividing the thorax into two halves.

Inside the chest the oesophagus passes over the upper part of the heart in close contact with its main artery, the aorta. Leaving the chest cavity the oesophagus penetrates the *diaphragm*, a strong muscular and fibrous partition which separates the thorax from the abdomen. The oesophagus reaches and joins up with the *stomach* at what is known as the *cardiac end* of this organ.

Large bloodvessels and nerves are to be found in the region of the neck. The common carotid artery conveys blood from the left ventricle of the heart to the head and upper part of the neck. The carotid artery ascends the neck, with the trachea, as far as the larynx, where it branches into three main vessels supplying the head and brain.

The jugular vein is a large vessel which drains blood *away* from the head and upper part of the neck. It passes out through the parotid gland, situated at the hinder corner of the lower jawbone, and travels down the jugular furrow in the neck, in close company with the carotid. On the left side of the neck it is closely related to the oesophagus.

Nerves emerge from between the cervical vertebrae but in addition the cerebral nerves, particularly the tenth nerve known as the *vagus*, run in company with the cervical cord of the *sympathetic* nerve, usually close to the carotid artery.

CHAPTER THREE

THE FORE LIMB

MOST breeders, and judges too, pay very great attention to the hind limbs, their grace of movement and the part they play in propulsion of the body. The majority pay far less attention, however, to the part which the fore limbs play in propulsion, with the fixed belief, apparently, that the hind legs do the pushing and that the fore legs are concerned mainly with support and play only a minor part in moving the body from place to place.

If a lightweight dog, a whippet for example, sustains some serious injury to its hind limbs and is allowed to live, it will not be long before it learns to elevate the hinder part of the body and walk about on its two forefeet alone with ease and speed.

A Dachshund, a breed which only too often loses the use of its hinder parts, would be unable to do as the whippet does, owing to a combination of very short forelegs and a lengthy body.

If an accident happens to the front end of the body involving both fore limbs, even in a dog as adaptable as a whippet, the hind limbs will be quite incapable of lifting the front end and moving the body from place to place in an erect or semi-erect position.

By means of an appliance which measures the force of the impact conveyed to the ground by each foot in turn (working somewhat on the principle of the treadmill) it can be shown that the fore limb supports not only rather more than the weight of the front half of the body but that it also possesses a power of propulsion, or traction whichever may be applicable, frequently greater than that transmitted by the hind limb.

It must be noted, however, that the force of impact of the fore foot upon the ground varies according to the position of the dog's head during movement.

The propulsive impact, in contrast with that registering the amount of bodyweight falling upon the ground through the foot, is greatest in dogs which hunt by sight with the head elevated and firmly anchored in that position by contraction of the neck muscles. This is essential in order to permit the muscles which travel the length of the neck, from skull to humerus, to pull the arm forward to its fullest extent.

The amount of propulsion exerted by the fore foot pressing upon the ground, decreases when the head is lowered, either from tiredness or for the purpose of scenting in hounds and gundogs. Such dogs when outside, with their freedom granted, propel themselves largely by the efforts of their hind limbs, with heads lowered, much in the same way that a man pushes a reluctant motor car by getting behind it and letting his limbs and feet stretch well behind him in order that the force transmitted to the body through the limbs shall travel along his spine, which will then be closely in alignment with the midline of the car.

However sound this may appear in theory, it is not always so sound when put into practice since the modern showdog has had to be re-shaped in order to make this kind of propulsion possible and the change of shape has thrown an undue stress upon parts of the body never designed for the purpose.

The fore limb can play any considerable part in propulsion only when it has freedom of action, that is to say when the fore foot can be brought into a fully advanced position well in front of the body, so that the latter may pass over the limb in the course of every forward stride in much the same way that the rim of a wheel passes over the hub (representing the ground), with the spoke of the wheel playing the part of the limb.

As stated earlier the limb can only be brought fully forward when the head is being carried high and firmly supported by the tensed muscles of the neck. This permits a considerably longer total stride with a corresponding increase in speed, provided that the number of strides per minute is not appreciably lessened.

The raising of the head and the extra forward reach of the fore limb greatly improves the appearance of the gait.

Some breeds such as Poodles and Italian Greyhounds which are (or in the case of the Poodles, were) supposed to parade around and up and down the ring with a hackney-like or dancing movement, make use of a muscle in the neck (the brachiocephalicus) which passes from the occipital bone and mastoid process of the skull down the neck to the middle of the shaft of the humerus. When the head is raised and held firmly in place by other neck muscles, contraction of this brachiocephalic muscle brings the knee and foot upwards and forwards with a slight jerk, and when this is compensated by other simultaneous limb movements the characteristic prancing stride seen in these breeds materialises.

All this requires the handing down, from the parents, a particularly well-developed brachiocephalic muscle, a well-inclined scapula which will probably accompany a long, strong neck, together with a sound, firmly-muscled forearm. It is a type of action which runs in certain strains specially bred with an eye to movement, but it is rarely seen in the pet Poodle mass-produced for the pet market.

Not the least important part of the fore limb lies below the knee and to get perfect front action the pasterns must be straight and strong with just the right amount of spring and give. The pads of the feet should be firm and thick and well spaced so that the weight falls upon them in the right places and there is no loss of the power transmitted through them when they encounter the ground surface.

The biceps muscle has its origin at the front of the shoulder below the shoulder joint and travels down the limb parallel with the humerus to be finally inserted into the upper ends of the front of the radius and ulna. It flexes the elbow and materially assists in drawing the fore leg forward, being opposed in " co-operative antagonism " by the triceps muscle, which lies behind the shoulder. It arises from the hinder edge of the scapula and is inserted into the olecranon process of the elbow. This muscle, when it contracts, forces the weight of the body to pass over the fore limb which will now be fixed in a state of momentary rigidity owing to the fact that the olecranon process of the ulna is being forced into the olecranon fossa at the lower end of the humerus.

The degree of solidity thus produced, converts the whole limb into a rigid prop during this important phase of every forward stride.

Let us now consider the bones of the fore limb and observe

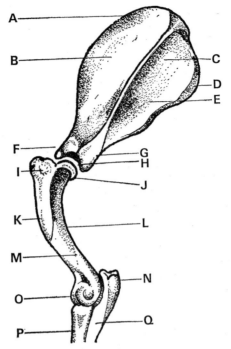

Fig. 18. The Scapula, Humerus and elbow joint

Scapula
A. *Cervical angle*
B. *Supraspinous fossa*
C. *Scapular spine*
D. *Dorsal angle*
E. *Infraspinous fossa*
F. *Coracoid process*
G. *Acromion process*
H. *Glenoid cavity*

Humerus
I. *External tuberosity*
J. *Articular head*
K. *Deltoid tubercle*
L. *Musculo-spiral groove*
M. *Shaft of humerus*

Ulna
N. *Olecranon process of ulna*
O. *Anterior lower articular surface*
P. *Radius*
Q. *Ulna*

From the conformation and exhibition angles, the shoulder joint is one of the most important in the dog's body.

The first essential is that the scapula shall be well inclined backwards along the spine, so far as its summit is concerned. The shoulder joint is a fixed point and it follows that the angle between the scapula and the humerus at its point of articulation must be as acute as possible.

The easy way to measure the degree of inclination through the skin by the use of the fingers is to place a finger of the left hand upon the shoulder joint which, incidentally, is the most prominent part of the trunk (that part of the body below the level of the neck) and a finger of the right hand upon the summit of the spine of the scapula, which can be recognized easily with a little practice, and estimate the angle this line makes with the ground upon which the dog is standing.

In a well-inclined shoulder such as the one illustrated, the angle is approximately forty-five degrees. In an upright shoulder the angle may be fifty-five degrees, or more. This means of measurement differs from that by which the line follows the spine of the scapula.

What is often not realized is that the angle at which the scapula is inclined depends not only upon the relative length of the cervical and dorsal vertebrae, more particularly that of the first six dorsal vertebrae, but also upon the degree of curvature of the first four ribs, or more accurately, perhaps, upon the point of their greatest curvature.

For instance, if these ribs are subject to much curvature, and especially if their curvature is present high up in each rib, the upper extremities of both scapulae are forced farther apart and when this happens, the scapula is forced into an upright position mainly because it is unable to slide backward over the curvature of the ribs. When one can place two or three fingers between the upper ends of the two scapulae with the head in the normal position in the standing dog, then it is almost certain that the shoulders will be both upright and too widely spaced at the withers. The difference between the two types of shoulder may be seen when one compares a coursing greyhound with one of modern exhibition type. The reason for the more upright shoulder with all its inconveniences, in the coursing dog, is that if the two scapulae were close together, the space between their summits being able to accommodate only the tip of one finger, the dog

might be very fast and a free mover in front, but it might be totally unable to lower its head sufficiently at a fast pace to pick up a hare. There are many exhibition greyhounds with beautifully inclined shoulders and long necks, that are unable to feed from a dish laid upon the ground in front of them unless they bend one knee, or straddle their front legs, so that their muzzles may reach down to the ground.

Incidentally, a long neck usually accompanies a well-inclined shoulder, because the cervical and dorsal bones are equally lengthy. The difficulty in many breeds such as the terriers, and some of the gundogs such as the Cocker spaniel, is that while the neck must be long and the scapula well inclined, in keeping with these elongated vertebrae, the dorsal bones, and more particularly the lumbar bones need to be inordinately short, so that the body may be short. The difficulty is to get these two contradictory features present in the same dog.

When a dog is walking fast, trotting or galloping, the fore limb can be advanced little beyond what would constitute a straight line with the scapula spine. It follows, therefore that the more inclined the scapula, the greater is the forward reach of the fore foot. This is pulled forward not only by the limb muscles but also by the brachiocephalic muscle which is fixed in front to the occipital bone and the mastoid process of the temporal bone and at its other end into the lateral aspect of the humerus, close below its articular head. The higher, within reason, that the head is carried, the farther forward can the limb be advanced.

how they influence the operative efficiency of the limb, with especial regard to the influence exerted by differences in the relative lengths of the various bones and their degree of inclination.

THE SCAPULA

This is a triangular, flat bone, a shape which enables it to cover and protect a wide surface, provide anchorage for a number of muscles which operate the limb and assist in neck movements, and incidentally, attach the fore limb to the body, the spine and the ribs, without the help of any bony structure whatever.

The thorax or rib cage is thereby suspended, as though in a cradle, between the two scapulae with considerable freedom of movement in all the parts involved.

On either side of the body the scapula is attached to the spine. Behind it is fastened to the ribs by muscle. Its under surface carries a flat muscle, the subscapularis, upon which it rides freely over the surface of the ribs beneath.

To complete the picture, the thorax is supported at its lowest part by the pectoral muscles which stretch from humerus to sternum.

The scapula of the dog differs from that of the horse in being without a " cartilage of prolongation " at its summit.

The spine of the scapula, a raised and prominent ridge of bone easily palpable through the skin of the shoulder, divides the external face of the bone into two parts, the anterior being slightly the wider except at its upper end where the front edge of the bone approaches the upper end of the scapular spine. The result is that the front edge of the dog's scapula represents a small portion of the arc of a circle.

Its hinder edge is almost straight from its upper or dorsal angle down to the acromion, the name given to a rather prominent tubercle on the lower end of the scapula spine. (*See Fig. 18*)

The lower end of the scapula contains the glenoid cavity, a rounded cup forming one half of the shoulder joint.

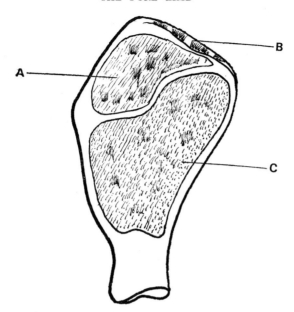

Fig. 19. Under surface of Scapula

The illustration shows how the scapula is attached to the body by muscles without any form of bony union.

The area (A) is occupied by the ventral portion of the serratus muscle which is inserted into the first seven or eight ribs. Just above this, the rhomboideus muscle is attached to the hinder half of the upper edge of the scapula (B) while its other end is attached to the ligamentum nuchae in the neck and to the spinal processes of the first two or three dorsal vertebrae.

The fossa in the under surface of the scapula below this (C), is occupied by the subscapularis muscle which is inserted into the upper end of the humerus medial to its articular head.

In addition to the attachments shown in this diagram, the outer surface of the scapula has attachments also.

The trapezius muscle is attached to the middle of the spine of the scapula and is inserted into the spinous processes of the dorsal vertebrae from the 3rd to the 10th.

The cervical portion of this same trapezius muscle is attached to the 1st, 2nd, 3rd, or 4th dorsal vertebrae.

The other half is the articular head of the humerus which fits it accurately, the two being held together by the capsular ligament, which is attached to the circumference of both articular surfaces, completely surrounding the joint.

The two upper ends of the scapulae are tilted slightly inwards by the pull of the muscles which join them to the dorsal vertebrae

F

If the tip of a finger be placed on the midline of the withers and pressed firmly down, it will pass between the upper edges of the two scapulae and come to rest on the dorsal spinous process beneath it, probably between the second and fourth of these. If, with the finger in this position, the dog's head be now pressed downwards to the ground, the finger tip may become tightly squeezed between the two scapular edges, especially in the exhibition Greyhound.

When the bones actually meet during this head-lowering process, the head can go no lower and in extreme cases in exhibition Greyhounds the dog will be unable to pick a hare or rabbit from the ground and may have difficulty in feeding from a dish set at ground level unless it stretches out its fore limbs or bends the knees.

It follows, therefore, that Greyhounds bred for coursing should come only from stock which has been previously tested and in which it is possible to insert the tips of two fingers between the scapulae with the head held downward.

The present Greyhound standard is wrong in requiring shoulders to be " narrow and clearly defined at the top ", if this causes difficulty in lowering the head.

The angle of inclination of the scapula is of great importance not only from the exhibition angle but also because only a dog with a properly inclined scapula can move freely and well. The degree of inclination depends mainly upon the length of the cervical and dorsal bones and this is why a long neck is usually accompanied by a well-laid scapula, while a short, erect neck goes in company with an upright scapula and often with what at least appears to be, a long back.

The reason why the degree of inclination of the scapula is dependent upon the length of the cervical and dorsal bones is that the scapula, whatever its length or degree of inclination, is attached always to the same dorsal vertebrae by the muscles which pass from the one to the other.

To exemplify this, the rhomboideus muscle, for instance, is attached at one end to the spinous processes of the fourth to seventh dorsal bones and at the other to the cervical angle of the scapula (its upper anterior angle).

Then, again, the trapezius muscle, a thin triangular sheet over-lying the scapular region, is in two parts. The cervical part is attached to the ligamentum nuchae and to the spinous processes of the second to fourth dorsal bones while at its other end it is inserted into the spine of the scapula. The dorsal portion also joins up with the spine of the scapula but it is also inserted into the tenth dorsal bone.

Although this may not appear too intelligible without being in a position to view the actual specimen, it will convey the impression that the scapula has a number of fixed attachment points. To obtain the necessary degree of inclination the upper end of the bone must lie as far back along the body as possible and this depends upon the neck and dorsal bones being sufficiently lengthy to extend back to the necessary position.

It is also a good thing if the scapula is flattened without a too well-developed scapular spine. The reason is that judges knock off marks for what they call " overloaded shoulders ". These may arise from shoulders being too upright but when present in a well laid-back shoulder it is usually because the scapular spine is too high with the production of a deep cavity on either side capable of carrying too great a load of muscle. Even a flat shoulder blade may on occasion develop excess of muscle but this can usually be traced to free exercise, with some galloping. It is something of an anomaly when one has to avoid anything more strenuous than walking in an exhibition Greyhound, a breed whose job it is to gallop, in case it should develop muscles for which it would have to be penalized.

THE HUMERUS

This bone which extends from the shoulder joint to the elbow is not a straight bone but slightly twisted in its length in the shape of an Italian f. In consequence of this slight torsion the bone carries on its outer aspect a shallow groove the length of the shaft. This is known as the musculo-spiral groove and it gives lodgement to the brachialis muscle which helps the biceps muscle flex the shoulder joint.

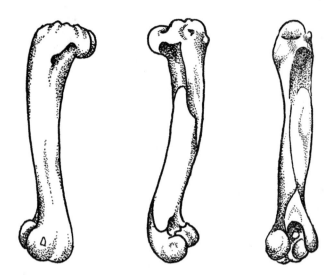

Fig. 20. Three views of the Humerus of the dog

The illustrations depict the humerus of a dog of terrier type, relatively lengthy. In the achondroplastic breeds, such as the Scottish terrier, the humerus may still be a stout bone but very much reduced in length so far as the shaft portion (diaphysis) is concerned. The joint portions (the epiphyses) may be very similar to those in the illustration.

The humerus lies in an inclined plane set at an angle of ninety-five degrees with the spine of the scapula and as the spine of the scapula is inclined at an angle of forty-two degrees, or thereabouts, it should be easy to work out the degree of inclination of the humerus. By actual measurements the average degree of inclination is forty-five degrees, but some slight variation will exist in the case of the straight front of a Fox terrier and that of a short-limbed Dachshund.

Features of the humerus of the dog

The upper end of the humerus carries an articular head, rounded, with a distinct neck. The head fits into the glenoid cavity of the scapula.

In front of the head is the external tuberosity, a bony mass which can be felt through the skin as it is the most prominent point of the shoulder.

The front of the external tuberosity bears a single groove in place of the bicipital (double) groove of the horse, and through this passes the upper tendon of the biceps muscle. Between the groove and the tendon is a synovial bursa and this is frequently injured and becomes a cause of lameness in Greyhounds and cattle dogs especially.

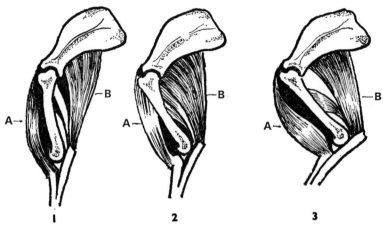

Fig. 21. The Muscles which operate the elbow joint

A. Biceps muscle   B. Triceps muscle

(1) The forelimb is being drawn forward (extended) by the combined action of the biceps and the brachiocephalus muscle which passes from the head, travels down the neck and is inserted in the shaft of the humerus.

Behind the limb, the triceps muscle is exerting sufficient opposing force to control the steady movement of the limb, and preventing sudden jerking with possible risk of bone fracture.

(2) The radius and ulna are now becoming locked at the elbow joint into a rigid prop by the combined pull of the biceps and triceps muscles in co-operative antagonism. The olecranon process of the ulna becomes locked in the olecranon fossa at the rear of the humerus.

(3) The elbow is now being released and is ready to go into flexion through the combined pull of the biceps and triceps with the biceps slightly dominant. In (2) the triceps was the dominant muscle.

The combined action of these two muscles are essential to forward movement of the body.

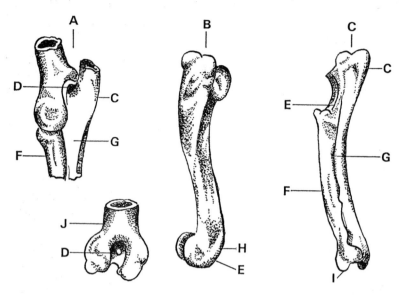

Fig. 22. *Humerus, radius and ulna in formation of elbow joint*

A. *Elbow joint*   B. *Humerus*   C. *Radius and Ulna*

A. *Elbow joint (locked)*   F. *Radius*
B. *Humerus*   G. *Ulna*
C. *Olecranon process*   H. *Lower end of humerus*
D. *Olecranon fossa*   I. *Lower articular sur-*
E. *Sigmoid cavity*   *faces of radius and ulna*

The illustration shows how the radius and ulna fit into the sigmoid cavity at the base of the humerus, permitting free movement during joint flexion but bringing it to a complete halt as regards further extension directly the limb, including the elbow and carpus, come into line. The object of this is to turn the fore limb into a rigid prop when weight falls upon the foot.

If by any chance the two bones, the radius and humerus were not perfectly fitted, the one into the other, so that the carpus permitted the lower part of the limb to slacken slightly, the limb would no longer be a straight prop when weight fell upon the foot, but the pastern and foot below the knee would slope forward and the dog would be said to possess slack pasterns.

This shows that defects from an exhibition standard, below the knee, may be due to maladjustment at the elbow joint. The bones portrayed are similar to those found in any normal dog but they may differ in many ways from the same bones in one of the toy, brachycephalic, or achondroplastic breeds such as the Griffon, Pekingese or the Scottish terrier, or even in a Cairn or a Sealyham.

In all the short-limbed breeds the humerus is similar as regards its joints or articulations but different as regards

The shaft of the humerus is slightly curved or spiral in shape according to breed and it carries at its lower end two sets of articular surfaces, one in front, the other behind.

The front articular surface takes the form of a double ridge with a groove separating the two.

At the back of the lower end of the humerus there is a deep fossa, the olecranon fossa, lying between the portions of bone which articulate below with the radius and ulna.

In the dog there is a perforation right through the depth of this fossa, communicating with the coronoid fossa which lies above the trochlea in front of the bone.

Into this deep olecranon fossa the olecranon process of the ulna fits when the elbow joint is extended (straightened) and as this is the position the limb always assumes in the standing position when weight is placed on the foot, it follows that the elbow joint is locked and will remain so until the weight is taken off the foot. This can be done by advancing the diagonal hind limb, or by swinging the thorax slightly towards the opposite side of the body which may be regarded as lying within a cradle provided by the two scapulae and the muscles passing between them and the spine, ribs and sternum.

When moving off from a standstill with both elbows locked, the dog usually transfers some of the body weight from the fore end to the hind by slightly flexing a hock and dropping the corresponding quarter, or alternatively, the hind limb may be advanced and the hock then flexed.

Either of these movements will take weight off the diagonally opposite fore limb and make it easier for the dog to advance it.

The length of the humerus plays an important part in determining the position of the elbows. When the humerus is relatively short the

---

the shaft of the bone, being in these breeds shorter and often relatively somewhat thicker.

The differences in the appearance of bones is so marked in the various types of dog that an expert looking at a single bone can usually say what breed of dog it came from.

Also certain differences, mainly as regards the chemical constitution of the bones may be detected in several breeds.

elbows must necessarily be positioned farther forward along the wall of the thorax than when the humerus is longer. Similarly, the length of the scapula must also play a part in deciding where the elbows will lie, but this is not so important as the degree of inclination of the scapula.

It would be hard to imagine a short scapula being markedly inclined since the upper end of the scapula is attached to a fixed point as regards the dorsal bones and such a combination would move the position of the shoulder joint too far back, whereas this joint is in reality the most prominent part of the front of the shoulder region.

The degree of inclination of the humerus must vary according to differences in its length. In the Fox terrier again, a dog with a straight front and very much on its toes, the elbows must lie well forward and not far behind the shoulder joint, and this will necessitate a shortening of the humerus. A Labrador, with elbows farther back under the chest, would need a longer humerus to make this possible.

Although the humerus is relatively long in most dogs it may become very much shortened in achondroplastic breeds such as the Scottish terrier and Dachshund, breeds in which the head bones remain comparatively large but those of the limbs are stunted. This is not identical with dwarfism in which the whole body is reduced in size and yet the relative lengths of all the bones is similar in the large and small varieties. This applies to the Poodles for instance, in which the toy specimens are reduced replicas of the miniature size, and the miniatures reduced replicas of the standards, at present alike in all respects apart from size. As time goes on no doubt each of the three types will develop characteristics of their own as the result of intensive breeding but this would not be in accordance with modern standards.

THE RADIUS AND ULNA

These bones of the fore arm are relatively long in the dog. The radius is much flattened from before to behind. The ulna is the longer and larger of the two bones mainly on account of its olecranon process which (*See Fig. 22*) extends for some distance above the upper end of the radius. The radius and ulna are articulated at the inner side of the head of the radius and at the lower end at the outer side of the radius, and between these two points a narrow interosseous space separates the two bones. The degree of movement between the two bones is practically negligible. The cat can rotate its paws and hold small objects between the palms of its front paws. This ability is less marked in the dog, although in young dogs there may be a little rotation of the radial head upon the ulna. In older dogs a certain amount of fusion usually occurs.

The olecranon process of the ulna is well developed and carries a smooth, semi-circular articular cavity below its anterior edge, for articulation with the lower end of the humerus. When the elbow is fully extended with the limb completely straightened, the beak of the olecranon process actually enters the olecranon fossa and locks the elbow joint.

The lower end of the ulna articulates with the cuneiform and pisiform bones of the carpus or knee. The radius does so with the remaining bones of the upper row.

The Carpus or Knee

This joint corresponds with the human wrist. It contains seven bones in the dog, three in the upper row and four in the lower. In the upper row the scaphoid and semilunar are fused to form a single large bone, the scapholunar. This articulates with the radius, the cuneiform articulates with both radius and ulna, and the pisiform with the ulna. The cuneiform, the outermost bone of the upper row, dips down into the second row to articulate with the external metacarpal bone. The trapezium articulates with the first and second metacarpals; the trapezoid with the second; the os magnum with the third, while the cuneiform articulates with the fourth and fifth metacarpal bones.

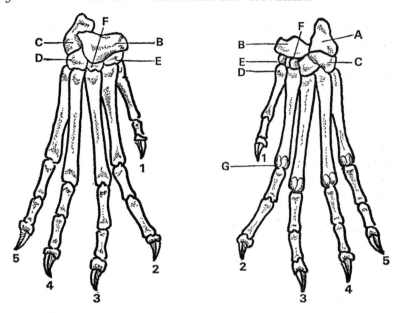

Fig. 23. The manus or knee, pastern and foot

Below the knee the metacarpal bones follow and in turn these are followed by the digits (2) and lastly by the small circles of bone which surrounds the root of each nail.

Bones of the Carpus	D. Unciform
A. Pisiform	E. Trapezoid
B. Scapulolunar bone	F. Os magnum
C. Cuneiform	

Metacarpus

Below the knee five bones are present, the first or innermost being much the shortest and the third and fourth the longest. The second is slightly shorter than the third and fourth and a little longer than the fifth, which is the thickest of them all.

At their upper ends all five bones are articulated to their neighbours and in passing downwards they diverge a little. Each metacarpal bone carries behind, two small sesamoids.

The Digits

There are five digits, as in the human hand. The innermost,

commonly called the " dewclaw ", has only two phalanges and does not make contact with the ground. The other four each have three phalanges. (*See Fig. 23*) The first and second phalanges are diminutive long bones. The terminal phalanx is small and hook-like and a collar of bone encircles its base. A terminal piece of bone, a small replica of the nail of the particular toe, fills the upper end of each toenail.

The Feet

Whatever the breed, the foot of the dog is a highly complicated structure designed to give support, prevent skidding and act as a surface-holding device working in unison with the braking action of the limb.

In addition to the large assortment of bones below the knee and hock which enter into its formation, a great number of muscles, extensors and flexors, with their tendons and accessory ligaments, play their part in maintaining stability and effecting body propulsion.

Not only the bones but also this intricate mechanism of muscles, tendons and ligaments, play their respective parts, too. They may affect the general shape of the foot, or produce variations in its shape according to the condition of the muscular tissue, tendons and ligaments at any particular time. Muscles become thicker and stronger if they are exercised, and also according to the nature of the ground on which the exercise takes place; whether it be rough, necessitating a bunching-up of the toes in order to negotiate it successfully, or if it be smooth and soft, making it possible for the dog to travel flat-footed without undue discomfort.

The result of these factors may be that feet which are nicely arched under some conditions may become slack and spread-out under others, not on account of any fault in the conformation of the dog.

In a similar way pasterns which are firm and erect as the result of regular exercise, may become relaxed and yielding when the

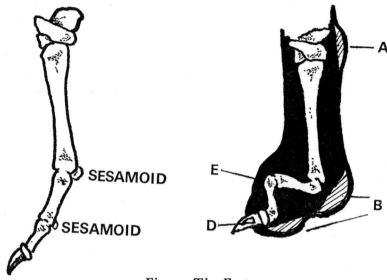

SESAMOID

SESAMOID

Fig 24. The Foot

(*A*) *A single metacarpal bone and phalanx removed from the limb.*
(*B*) *The same, within the foot. In the so-called " cat-foot", the bones within the foot are set at an acute angle, as above.*
   In " hare feet ", the angulation is less marked and the angle at (E) may be almost obliterated in extreme cases.
   The pad behind the knee, is known in racing circles as the " stopper " and it is believed that racing greyhounds use these pads as brakes, when pulling up. Not uncommonly, they may be partially pulled off the leg in the process.

A. *Pads*
B. *Pads*
D. *Nail*

dog is confined for the greater part of each day in a kennel or even in a dwelling house.

   There are two main types of feet :

   (a) Those seen in terriers, the toes bunched together like those of a cat. This is brought about partly by muscular contraction and partly by shortened ligaments.

   (b) In some breeds tight bunching of the toes is not characteristic, the feet being flattened and more lengthy like those of a hare. In these the ligaments between the bones of the feet are slacker and this enables the terminal joints to extend slightly.

   In some breeds the fore feet are more or less cat-like and the hind feet of the hare type.

Breeds in which the feet are not definitely of cat type include:
The Samoyed, Tibetan Spaniel, Chihuahua, Italian Greyhound,
Japanese, Papillon, Pug and Saluki.

Cat-feet are seen in the Terrier family and in the exhibition
Greyhound but less frequently in the coursing dog.

The pads of the feet are modified areas of skin, five in number.
Four of these, the smaller pads; oblong with their long axis coin-
ciding with that of the body, or rounded, according to the breed;
are attached beneath the terminal joint of each digit.

The largest pad lies in the hollow of the digits between the
other four pads, being more or less heart-shaped, with its apex
directed towards the centre of the under surface of the foot. This
large pad receives a branch from the tendon of the deep flexor
tendon of the foot.

Above the foot and at the back of the limb at the level of the lower
row of carpal bones is another well-developed pad-like structure,
rather loosely attached by skin and directed downwards. In coursing
dogs it is known as the " stopper " and it appears to be used in
" braking " down from speed. It is often torn partly away from the
limb when acting in this way.

Usually the pads are black or darkly pigmented but in some
white dogs they may be flesh-coloured and devoid of pigment
(often in company with the nose). In such cases the nails may also
be unpigmented.

The nail is secreted by a coronary band surrounding its base.
The bone of the final digit carries a small circle of bone above
each bony nail core, a smaller replica of each nail. This bone
carries minute laminae to which the nail is attached. Each
nail continues to grow an excess of terminal horn unless this
is worn down by constant nail friction with the ground surface,
or cut short with shears. When the large central pad is thin the tips
of the toes are liable to be directed slightly upwards with the result
that the nails continue to grow without wearing down from friction
with the ground surface.

When growth is excessive the horny excess may eventually form
a circle or a spiral and may even sink into the skin of the foot.
This can happen only when the nail is making insufficient contact

with the ground and it is especially common in the case of the " dewclaws " which never touch the ground. Excessive nail growth is common when the central heart-shaped pad of the foot is thin or badly-developed so that the small pads lift the front of the foot and the nails turn upwards instead of downward. If the central pad is quite thick, the reverse is the case. The nails then point downward and become worn down by contact with the ground.

CHAPTER FOUR

THE THORAX

The body is divided into two portions, the chest or thorax and the abdomen. The two are separated internally by the dome-shaped muscular and tendinous partition, known as the *diaphragm*. The chest walls are lined and the lungs covered by a membrane known as the pleura. The thorax is divided longitudinally by a partition of pleura, known as the mediastinum.

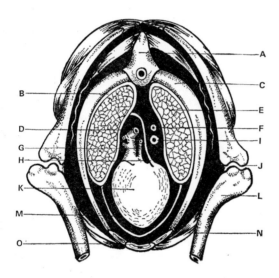

Fig. 25. Section of Chest

The thorax is suspended between the two scapulae and the ribs entirely by muscular attachment without any form of bony union. At the lower end it is supported and also moved from side to side between the arm bones, as though held in a cradle.

A. Dorsal vertebra	F. Oesophagus	K. Heart
B. Pleura	G. Aorta	L. Humerus
C. Rib	H. Pulmonary artery	M. Peritoneum
D. Mediastinum	I. Vena Cava	N. Pectoral muscles
E. Lung	J. Shoulder joint	O. Sternum

The Diaphragm

Viewed from the abdominal side, the diaphragm is concave in all directions. It consists of a tendinous, glistening centre surrounded by muscles which cause the diaphragm to become flattened and convex (at the thoracic side) alternately.

As the space between the lungs and the rib lining (pleura) and the diaphragm behind contains nothing but a potential vacuum, the lungs expand and contract, in close contact with the movements of ribs and diaphragm and in this way air fills the lungs during inspiration and is forced out during expiration.

If by any chance a wound between the ribs should permit the free passage of air into the potential space between the covering of the lungs (*visceral pleura*) and the lining of the chest (*parietal pleura*), the lungs would no longer follow the rib movements and so they would collapse, cease to draw in air and the dog would die from asphyxia.

The central tendinous portion of the diaphragm is perforated to allow the passage of the oesophagus through it, to immediately join the stomach on its abdominal side. In addition the diaphragm gives passage to the aorta and other large bloodvessels and nerves.

The Ribs

In the dog the ribs number thirteen pairs of which nine pairs are united below to the sternum (breast bone). The tenth, eleventh and twelfth pairs are united below to each other by a cartilaginous prolongation of each rib while the thirteenth pair, known as floating ribs are free at their lower terminations.

Each rib is an elongated, more or less curved and highly elastic bone. At its upper end it carries an articular head which articulates with *two* dorsal vertebrae except in the case of the first rib which articulates with the last cervical and first dorsal bones. Just behind the articular head is another projection known as the tubercle. This carries a flat articular surface which articulates with a similar surface on the transverse process of a dorsal vertebra.

The head and tubercle diminish in size from the first rib to the last.

The eighth pair of ribs are usually the longest and the ribs become progressively shorter as they run forward and backward from this eighth pair.

The longer the ribs, the deeper the chest, and the greater their

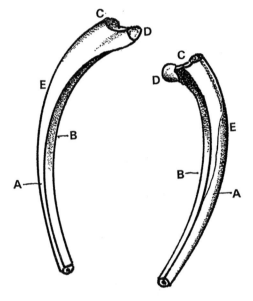

Fig. 26. Ribs of dog

A. *Inner surface*
B. *Anterior edge*
C. *Tubercle of rib*
D. *Articular head*
E. *Angle of rib*

degree of curvature the greater will be its cubic capacity. Modern standards require long ribs to provide a deep chest.

The Sternum

The sternum or breast bone is situated medially below the first nine pairs of ribs which join it on either side.

G

In reality, although described as a single bone, it consists of a number of bony segments joined together by cartilage.

In the dog there are eight of these segments and the cartilages uniting them together persist until late life when they become calcified into bone.

Until recent years each of the bony segments was compressed from side to side and slightly constricted in the middle.

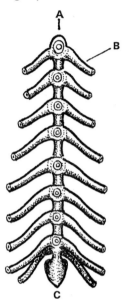

Fig. 27. Sternum of dog

A. *Body of segment, one*   B. *Rib cartilages*
  of eight carrying nine   C. *Xiphoid cartilage*
  pairs of ribs

Nowadays, as the result of selective breeding each segment is becoming deeper while (in Dachshunds and in some other breeds as Greyhounds and gundogs generally) there is a tendency to the development of a cartilaginous carina or keel, which gives the chest a fictitious appearance of greater depth, without in any way increasing the cubic capacity of the thorax.

The terminal part of the keel of the sternum is slightly flattened to form a xiphoid process, of about the size of a shilling. Just above this, in the thorax, lies the apex of the heart.

The Lungs

Each lung is a soft and spongy organ almost completely filling one side of the thoracic cavity, apart from the area occupied by the heart and bloodvessels.

Deep fissures extending through the lung substance right down to its roots, divide the lungs into separate lobes. The left lung is completely divided into two parts and the more anterior of these is partially sub-divided in its turn. The right lung has three lobes completely separated from one another.

The lateral (external) or costal surface of each lung is covered by a smooth, glistening *visceral pleura*. This is applied closely to the curvature of the ribs and the lungs may bear the impressions caused by such close contact.

The mediastinum, dividing the thorax longitudinally, opens out below (above the sternum) into what is known as the cardial mediastinum which contains the heart, surrounded by its own *pericardium*, a " bag " of pleura.

The Heart

The heart is a hollow, muscular pump, designed to pump blood through the bloodvessels throughout the body. It is shaped like an irregular cone lying obliquely in the thorax. Its apex looks downward and lies slightly to the left of the midline of the dia-phragm almost over the xiphoid cartilage of the sternum. Its base lies beneath the vertebral column and points towards the entrance to the thorax between the ribs. The heart lies between the two lungs so closely that a depression exists in each lung on the inner surface and into this depression the heart fits.

In its general appearance and shape the heart of the dog is much like that of other carnivora and as other quadruped hearts do, it contains two muscular ventricles which propel the blood, and two auricles which receive it and pump it into the ventricles through valves made of leaf-like " cusps ". Between the left auricle and the left ventricle there are two cusps in the valve (dicuspid) and between the right auricle and right ventricle there are three cusps (tricuspid).

The two auricles form the base of the heart and they are separated from the ventricles below them by a groove, the coronary groove, which contains the coronary vessels which feed the heart muscle with blood.

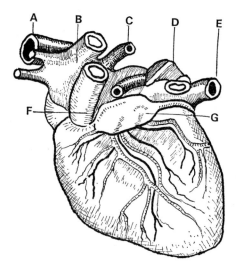

Fig. 28. Left side of heart
The dark vessels are veins, the light arteries

A. Cranial vena cava	D. Pulmonary veins	G. Left auricle
B. Aorta	E. Posterior vena cava	
C. Vena azygos	F. Pulmonary artery	

The right ventricle pumps the " used " blood through the lungs where it is reoxygenated. The blood returns into the left auricle through the pulmonary veins and is then driven into the left ventricle and throughout the body to supply its needs. It returns to the right auricle to recommence its journey.

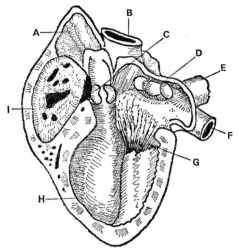

Fig. 29. Section of right side of heart

A. *Right auricle*
B. *Vena cava cranialis*
C. *Semilunar valves*
D. *Left auricle*
E. *Pulmonary veins*
F. *Vena cava caudalis*
G. *Bicuspid valve*
H. *Left ventricle*
I. *Right ventricle*

A lot is heard about the need for " heart room ". It is also generally supposed that the heart as its " beats ", jumps about inside the thorax. Actually it moves very little apart from a slight movement of the apex and the filling and emptying of its auricles and ventricles. What is really needed is lung room and this can only be possible when there is enough space *between* the ribs. Depth of chest is of far less consequence, other than in the showring.

CHAPTER FIVE

THE ABDOMEN

This portion of the body contains together with other important structures—arteries, veins and nerves—the following main organs:

Liver   Spleen
Stomach and duodenum   Bladder
Pancreas   The sex organs, Male and Female.
Small and large intestines   Kidneys and suprarenals

The Liver

This is a large, solid organ of chocolate colour, fitting accurately into the concave abdominal face of the diaphragm. It lies largely under cover of the ribs but usually a considerable quantity of its bulk projects into the abdomen behind the last ribs.

The liver is divided into three main lobes: a central, left lateral and right lateral.

The *gall-bladder* is a pear-shaped sac fitting into a deep depression in the liver and usually in contact with the pylorus (outlet) of the stomach.

The Stomach

The stomach represents a dilatation of the alimentary canal lying between the oesophagus (which enters it at its cardiac end) and the small intestine. In a Greyhound it holds four to five pints but when contracted and empty it appears very small.

When partly filled, the stomach will be seen to be divided into two parts:

(1) A wide body, resting mainly in the concavity of the diaphragm.

(2) A narrow pyloric portion extending into the duodenum on the right side of the body.

The pylorus is the terminal end of the stomach, acting like a valve, dilating sufficiently to permit partly digested food to enter the duodenum and closing tightly at other times.

Principally in large breeds, the stomach may fill with gas under pressure and rotate, cutting off all entry and exit. If not treated surgically at short notice, the condition is usually fatal.

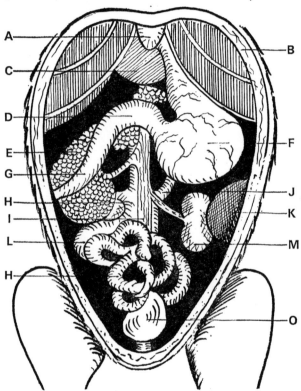

Fig. 30. Diagrammatic representation of the contents of the abdomen

A. Sternum	*F. Stomach*	*K. Spleen*
B. Wall of thorax	*G. Duodenum*	*L. Right Kidney*
C. Liver	*H. Small intestine*	*M. Left Kidney*
D. Pylorus	*I. Vena Cava*	*O. Bladder*
E. Pancreas	*J. Large intestine*	

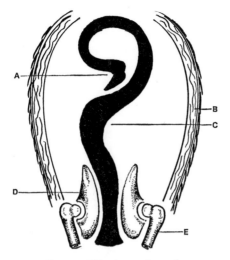

Fig. 31. The large intestine

The diagram shows the position of the large intestine in the dog's abdomen.

This is how the large bowel appears, after a barium enema, in an x-ray photograph.

The dog is lying on its back.

The large intestine takes the form of a question mark. In the pregnant female after the third week of gestation, the bowel becomes pushed to one side by the enlarging uterus. The same thing happens in a case of pyometra when the uterus is filled with a discharge. X-ray examination is therefore useful as a diagnostic agent in such instances.

The appendage at the upper end of the bowel is the caecum. The small intestine opens into the caecum at the ileo-caecal valve but is not shown in the diagram as it is seldom visible in an x-ray film unless the barium is given by mouth.

A. Caecum
B. Body wall
C. Large intestine

D. Pelvis
E. Femur

The Duodenum

Leaving the pyloric end of the stomach, the duodenum lies on the right side of the abdomen, and above the bulk of the small intestine.

The duodenum after leaving the pylorus, curves firstly upwards and to the right, making contact with the liver. It then descends and passes along the right side of the abdomen bending again to the left and becoming continuous with the remainder of the small intestine, which comprises the jejunum followed by the ileum.

The Pancreas

This important glandular structure has two main functions.

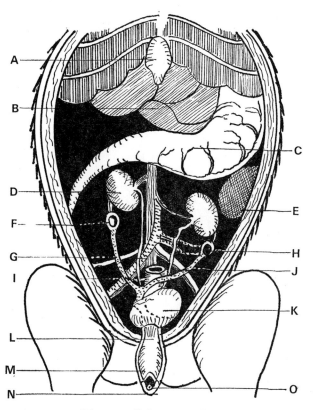

Fig. 32. Abdomen of bitch

A. Sternum	F. Right Ovary	K. Bladder
B. Liver	G. Right cornu of uterus	L. Vagina
C. Stomach	H. Left Ovary	M. Vestibule
D. Right kidney	I. Rectum	N. Vulva
E. Left Kidney	J. Left cornu of uterus	O. Clitoris

Firstly, it secretes digestive juices which are essential to nutrition. Secondly, it produces insulin which is also essential to existence.

In the dog the pancreas is an elongated, lobular gland, with two limbs that diverge from the region of the pylorus. The right limb is contained within the mesentery of the duodenum.

The pancreas may have two or three ducts which open into the duodenum, generally with the bile duct.

The Small Intestine

The duodenum is the first part of the small intestine. The remainder consists of the *jejunum* and the *ileum*.

The coils of small intestine are suspended from the dorsal wall of the abdomen by a fold of peritoneum known as the *mesentery* which resembles a thin, transparent fan, carrying a large number of bloodvessels.

The total length of the small intestine is approximately five times the length of the dog's body, when uncoiled.

The Large Intestine

Only a little greater in calibre than the small intestine in the dog, the length is only one sixth of that of the latter.

The large intestine follows the small intestine and commences at the *ileo-caecal valve*, the point at which the terminal portion of the small intestine enters the caecum at almost a right angle.

The caecum in the dog is small as compared with that of herbivorous animals, and takes the form of a short, bent and spiral tube with its free blind end directed backwards.

The large intestine, takes the shape in the dog of a large " question mark " occupying the length and width of the abdominal floor. It is divided into three parts, an ascending, a transverse and a descending portion. When a dog is given a barium injection and X-rayed, lying on its back, the large intestine can be seen to adopt this peculiar shape. When there is any enlargement of the uterus such as occurs in pyometra and in late pregnancy, the large intestine becomes pushed somewhat to one or other side and on X-ray examination the " question mark " disappears.

The Spleen

This is a solid organ, applied on one of its surfaces to the wall of the stomach to which it is bound by means of a ligament. This surface is concave. The opposite dorsal surface is convex and is applied to the lower surface of the spinal bones and the under surfaces of the ribs, extending a short way behind their borders. It is often the first organ to present itself when the abdomen is opened surgically along the midline. In the dog the spleen is from three to six inches long according to breed and size, a greyish-pink in colour and rather freely movable in the abdomen.

It is apt to undergo pathological enlargement. One removed three years ago from a Spaniel weighed ten pounds and the dog is still perfectly fit and lives a normal life.

It appears to be an organ one can live without, although it manufactures red corpuscles. After its removal the corpuscles are derived from the bone marrow.

The Bladder

This organ lies at the entrance to the pelvis when empty but protrudes into the abdomen when full of urine. Ventrally, it lies on the wall of the abdomen in contact with both the large and small intestines.

The two ureters, one from each kidney, open into the dorsal portion of the neck of the bladder.

In the male dog the two deferent ducts, those which carry the semen from the testicles to the urethral portion of the penis, lie upon the upper portion of the neck of the bladder within a triangular fold of mucous membrane.

These are, of course, absent in the bladder of the bitch. In the male, a sex gland, the prostate, a rounded, yellowish mass, surrounds the neck of the bladder. Usually only a small portion of it lies within the pelvis. The urethra passes through the prostate, and as in the dog the gland is subject to enlargement it often causes trouble.

THE MALE GENERATIVE ORGANS

Testicles

The testicles are slightly flattened oval bodies each contained in its own half of the scrotum which is divided by a partition. Each testicle runs upwards and backwards.

The dorsal border of each testis is connected with the epididymis and the extremities with the spermatic cords.

The epididymis is large in the dog and is formed by a long tube closely wound. On their way from the testicle through this tube the sperms undergo many changes which are necessary for fertility.

The Spermatic Cord

This consists of the spermatic duct (the vas deferens) which comes from the epididymis, the spermatic artery and veins, nerves and lymphatic vessels. The vein is rolled in a spiral and the whole of these are contained within a tunic which is derived from the peritoneum, the lining of the abdomen. The two cords pass down a channel in the abdominal wall known as the inguinal canal and together with the testicle and epididymis enter the scrotum, each on its own side.

The Inguinal Canal is a short, oblique passage about thirty millimetres long, having an internal opening between the muscles of the belly wall and an external opening also issuing between muscles.

In the bitch the canal contains no cord but the round ligament of the uterus passes from the tip of the uterine horn down the canal and is attached at its lower end within the skin of the vulva.

In inguinal hernia in the bitch the uterus descends into a peritoneal pouch lying in the groin.

The Prepuce

This is a tubular sheath lined with a modified skin, communicating with the exterior by a slit-like orifice. Within it lies the anterior glans of the penis composed of erectile tissue and when quiescent, completely covered by the prepuce.

The skin lining the prepuce is continued backwards to behind the posterior glans of the penis (described later) and then reflected forwards to cover the penis, joining up at the orifice at the tip of the penis with the mucous membrane of the urethra (the passage for urine).

The Penis

This consists of a *root* attached to the ischial bones of the pelvis, a body or middle portion containing spongy cavities (corpus spongiosum and corpus cavernosum) both packed with blood-vessels which when filled tightly with blood cause erection of the penis; and two erectile glans, the anterior and the posterior. The posterior is termed the " bulb " of the penis. In the dog the anterior glans is not so large as the posterior which enlarges very greatly during coitus and causes " locking ", the greatly swollen posterior glans becoming trapped within the vulva by the contractile, circular muscle surrounding the terminal part of the vagina.

The penis of the dog contains a bone, the os penis. This consists of two narrow plates, several inches long, joined dorsally to form a gutter in which the urethra lies, more or less surrounded by the corpus cavernosum. The portion of the urethra within the os penis,

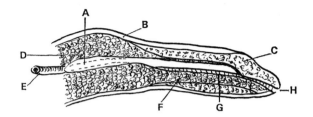

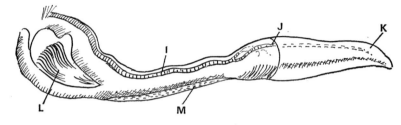

Fig. 33. The Penis

(below) External view of   D. Corpus cavernosum   I. Dorsal artery of penis
    penis   E. Urethra   J. Posterior glans
                                       F. Corpus spongiosum   K. Anterior glans
A. Os penis   G. Urethra lying within L. Erector muscles
B. Posterior glans   os penis   M. Retractor muscle
C. Anterior glans   H. Orifice of urethra

surrounded by the corpus cavernosum is smaller in diameter than
the portion behind the os. This is where bladder stones (calculi)
usually become arrested, and cause inability to pass urine.

THE FEMALE GENERATIVE ORGANS

The vulva of the bitch is a vertical slit with a blunt, rounded
dorsal commissure and a sharp, pointed, ventral commissure. Lying
within the lips of the latter is a rounded mass of erectile tissue,
the clitoris, and two elongated masses of erectile tissue known as
the vestibular bulbs. The lips of the vulva, on either side of the slit,
are termed the labia pudenda.

The Vagina

In the bitch this is a long tube lying between the neck of the uterus almost to the vulva. The intervening portion at the entrance to the vagina is smooth and is known as the *vestibule*. The surface of the vagina itself, behind the vestibule, is somewhat ridged by longitudinal folds of mucous membrane.

The orifice of the urethra (short in the bitch) opens out on the floor of the vestibule.

The Uterus

In the bitch this takes the shape of the letter Y, the two portions of the fork being much longer than the stem (the body of the uterus).

The elongated portions are known as the cornua, or horns.

The cavity of the body of the uterus is small and that of the horns apparently almost absent except during oestrus and pregnancy. Normally only a few inches in length and little thicker than a lead pencil for the greater part of the year, the uterus enlarges somewhat during oestrus. During pregnancy, the uterus of a bitch the size of a Cocker Spaniel may be capable of holding the equivalent of up to one and a half pints of water.

Fig. 34. Section through one mammary gland of bitch,

Showing the glandular structure and the
tubules leading to multiple teat orifices.

The Ovaries

These lie close to the kidneys to which they are loosely attached by a fold of peritoneal tissue known as the *mesovarium*, which joins up with a similar fold attached to the kidney known as the *mesometrium*.

Each ovum is enclosed in a *bursa* (meaning " a purse ") and the ovum itself can only be seen after this bursa has been divided.

During oestrus the ovum carries a number of vesicles containing fluid and an ovum or egg. These vesicles are also known as " *follicles* ".

Connecting each ovary to the end of the corresponding uterine horn is a ligamentous band, known as " *the proper ligament of the ovary* ".

The two kidneys lie at different levels. The left ovary lies *close* to the left kidney but the right is more loosely attached to the right kidney. This becomes very obvious during the operation of *hysterectomy* (speying).

The Kidneys

These are located against the dorsal wall of the abdomen and in a well-fed animal they are often surrounded by fat. Each kidney gives off an excretory tube known as the *ureter* which connects with the bladder and in addition each kidney carries in its hilus (ventrally placed depression) one of the two *suprarenal* or *adrenal glands*, embedded in fat.

Each kidney is rounded on its dorsal and lateral aspects but its medial border is straighter and notched by the *hilus* which leads into a small cavity, the *renal pelvis*, which is continuous with the *ureter*.

H

CHAPTER SIX

THE HIND LIMB

The degree of propulsion exercised by the hind limbs of the dog varies a great deal in accordance with the position of the head at the time.

When the head is carried low with nose to ground, the attitude adopted by gundogs at work, the greater propulsive force comes from the hind limbs, while the fore limbs often support considerably more than half the weight of the body. When the head is carried high with the dog trotting along, both the fore and the hind limbs are contributing to propulsion and sharing fairly equally in carrying weight, and in a dog provided with sloping shoulders and a good neck the fore limbs are sometimes more important than the hind. These (the fore limbs) are being drawn forward not only by the muscles of the shoulder but also by those of the neck, particularly the brachycephalic muscle which extends from skull to humerus, running down the whole length of the neck.

When the fore limb is carried as far forward as possible with the foot anchored firmly on the ground, the elbow joint locks, and henceforth the body has to pass over the elbow and the remainder of the limb, the latter playing the same part as the spokes of a wheel, with elbow as the hub or centre point, and the foot as the rim of the wheel.

It follows, too, that when the conformation of the front half of the body is very good and the front stride correspondingly long, the hindquarters and hind limbs must be equally strong, since in order to get the best results and perfect action, the hinder parts will need to increase their power of propulsion in order to keep on terms with greater length of the forward stride.

Of late years the tendency has been to demand angulation. This implies a flexed hip and stifle, extra length of the tibia and a shortening of the hindlimb from hock to foot.

During rest, the hind foot is then placed on the ground several inches behind a line dropped perpendicularly from the seat bone of the pelvis (tuber ischii) to the ground.

When a man pushes a motor car he can exert greater power if he goes behind the car, places his hands with arms fully extended on the rear of the car and extends his legs backwards so that his feet meet the ground, as far behind the car as his legs permit.

This is exactly what breeders have tried to do by increasing angulation, and placing the feet of the dog behind its body instead of beneath it.

While this may be successful in the comparatively slow-moving gundog, the same does not always apply in the faster dogs such as the Alsatians and the Greyhounds, but for totally different reasons in these two particular breeds.

In the Alsatian the lengthening of the tibia and the change of direction in the application of power has introduced some side-effects, not all to the good.

In the first place the thrust into the hip joint from the head of the femur has changed direction so that the line of force now encounters the rounded cup of the acetabulum at nearer nine o'clock where before it was nearer ten-thirty o'clock.

This puts an additional strain on the short " round ligament " which holds the head of the femur firmly in the acetabulum.

It also necessitates a different pattern in the type of muscular activity which controls the hindlimb and directs its force onto the wall of the acetabulum. In the original type of dog the pelvic muscles had the task of holding together the component parts of the hip joint, with a comparatively short hind stride which produced very little movement of the head of the femur.

Today, in the angulated specimen, the hind foot moves forward from a considerable distance behind the body to an equally considerable distance in front of it. This throws a great deal more strain on the joint surfaces.

In the running dogs such as the Greyhound, the change, whatever it has produced in the matter of appearance, has certainly done nothing to improve performance. The racing Greyhound of today has a straight hindlimb and tibia of moderate length and it executes a large number of short, rapid strides, attaining a very high speed.

The exhibition Greyhound with exaggerated angulation, " standing over a lot of ground ", and with a very much longer hind stride, both behind and beneath the body, actually carrying the hind feet past the shoulders in the forward section of the stride, cannot catch the smaller dog with the straighter, stifle and hock, simply because the fewer, longer strides cannot compete with the many shorter ones.

In the slower gundog the longer tibia and propulsion from behind the body, may have some advantage when the head is held low, but none when the dog is galloping.

What part angulation plays in the causation of hip dysplasia is a matter for speculation but there is one aspect that deserves attention.

In the original type of limb the muscle of the quarters covered the pelvis and played a main part in keeping the bones of the hip joint in firm apposition, even during movement. Muscle mass has been said to have a direct connection with the incidence of hip dysplasia and it has been asserted that the greater the muscular covering of the pelvis, the less chance there is of hip dysplasia developing in the growing puppy. This theory, however, is now disputed.

When the tibia becomes longer, with the hind feet well behind the body, the muscle mass covering the pelvis becomes less, since the muscles are not exercised as formerly they were, and the muscles now mainly employed are the gastrocnemius behind the limb, and the rectus femoris and vasti in front of it. These give rise to increased joint movement between the head of the femur and the cup of the acetabulum, but the muscle mass overlying the joint, and keeping its parts in apposition, is less in the over-angulated dog than in the normal limb.

The Pelvis

As in other animals, the pelvis of the dog consists of three bones

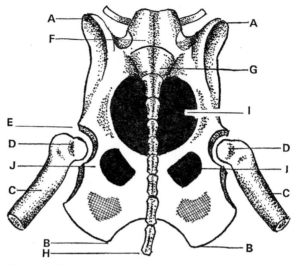

Fig. 35. The Pelvis and Hip joints (seen from above)

A. External angles of the
   ilium (haunch bone)
B. The ischium
C. The femur
D. The articular head of
   the femur

E. The acetabulum
   (articular surface of the
   pelvis)
F. The last lumbar verte-
   bra
G. The sacrum

H. The cocoygeal verte-
   brae (tail bones)
I. The cavity of the pelvis
J. The obturator foramen

fused together. The whole forms the innominate bone, and the two innominate bones placed side to side form the framework of the pelvic cavity.

The three bones comprising the pelvis are the ilium, the ischium and the pubis.

The *ilium* is the largest of the three divisions of the innominate bone. It is irregular in shape and forms the uppermost portion of the pelvic girdle. The gluteal (outer) surface is flattened and deeply depressed centrally. There is no very prominent angle of the croup in the dog as there is in the horse.

The *ischium* forms the posterior part of the pelvic floor and the two halves join the *pubis*, the anterior portion of the pelvic floor, the two halves of the floor being united by a cartilaginous layer which eventually becomes calcified into solid bone. In the dog this bony union does not become complete until some time

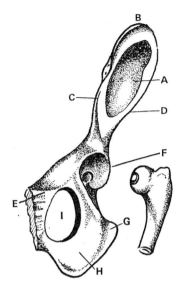

Fig. 36. Pelvis and hip joint (lateral view)

A. Gluteal surface of   D. Ischiatic edge of ilium   G. Tuber ischii
      ilium   E. Pubis   H. Ischium
B. Iliac crest   F. Acetabulum which   I. Oburator foramen
C. Pubic edge of ilium   receives head of femur

> Lower portion of pelvic bone showing the
> cup of the acetabulum with its notch for the
> insertion of the ligamentum teres (round
> ligament), together with the head of the femur
> which fits into the cup, and the notch in its
> articular head which gives attachment to the
> other end of the ligament.

after adult age has been reached. The union is termed the *Ischio-pubic symphysis.*

Between the pubis and the ischium on the pelvic floor is a large aperture, the obturator foramen and through this pass the bloodvessels and nerves to the hindlimb.

The transverse diameter of the pelvic cavity of the dog is much greater behind than in front.

The shape of the pelvic orifice varies a great deal in different breeds depending largely upon the length of the ilium. For example in an Airedale terrier the pelvic orifice in the bitch, the aperture through which a puppy has to pass is much higher than wide.

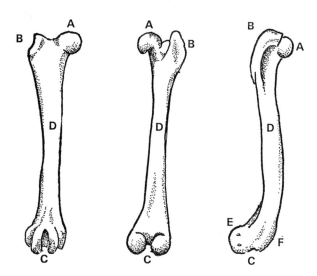

Fig. 37. The Femur

A. *Articular head*   D. *Shaft*
B. *Great trochanter*   E. *Condyle*
C. *Lower articular surface* F. *Trochlea* (*articulates with patella*)

In a Scottish terrier it may be square in shape rather than oblong due to shortening of all the limb bones, including the ilium.

The upper end of the ilium makes an articulation with the sacrum, the most solid portion of the lumbar spine and the sacrum thus forms the roof of the pelvic girdle.

On the outer side of the pelvic shaft near the pelvic floor is the *acetabulum*, the socket into which the head of the femur fits, a true ball-and-socket joint. It is made up from the junction of all three bones which form the pelvis. It contains at the anterior part a sulcus, a well defined notch open at the front end. This gives attachment to the teres ligament, or round ligament, which holds the head of the femur in its socket. It is only an inch in length, or less, and through its centre passes a bloodvessel which feeds the portion of the head of the femur directly in contact with the surface of the acetabulum.

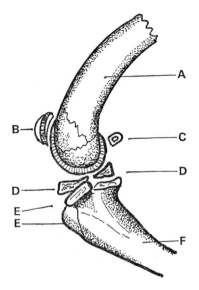

Fig. 38. Stifle joint of six-months puppy

A. Femur   D. Semilunar cartilage   F. Tibia
B. Patella   E. Epiphyses (not yet
C. Fabella   united)

The Femur

The thigh bone is much longer in the dog and also narrower than in the large domestic animals, and its shape is more curved.

The great trochanter lies at the upper end near the head but at the lower level. This prominence gives attachment to the muscles of the quarter.

The head of the femur which fits into the acetabulum is rounded in the dog. It has a well-marked neck and the head carries a rather shallow notch which gives attachment to the short teres ligament* which with the help of the muscles of the quarter, keeps the head of the femur tightly held within the cup of the acetabulum.

In cases of hip dysplasia, the head of the femur loses its circular shape and becomes conical. It is then able to move too freely in the acetabulum which also loses its rounded shape and becomes shallow and flattened, allowing the femur to " wobble " in its seating. This

* Another name for the " round ligament "

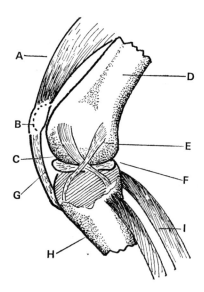

Fig. 39. Another view of the stifle joint

A. *Rectus femoris muscle*   D. *Femur*   G. *Straight ligament of*
B. *Position of patella*   E. *Posterior cruciate liga-*   *patella*
C. *Anterior cruciate iga-*   *ment*   H. *Tibia*
   ment   F. *Semilunar cartilage*   I. *Gastrocnemius muscle*

condition is not usually congenital but develops during growth of the puppy, or it may not appear until the second year, or in some cases, later.

Usually it affects both hips but may occasionally be confined to one side. As previously mentioned, the teres or round ligament contains a small artery which nourishes the head of the femur, or more correctly, the portion more deeply imbedded in the acetabulum. Although it is not a generally accepted theory, any fault in the circulation to the femoral head might easily affect its development and its shape.

The lips of the trochlea of the femur are of equal height in the dog but occasionally the outer is slightly higher than the inner, resulting in a tendency to a slipping patella. On the posterior aspect of the lower end of the femur there is a small pisiform bone known as the *fabella*, playing the part of a sesamoid to the gastrocnemius muscle. The patella is small and largely contained within the tendon

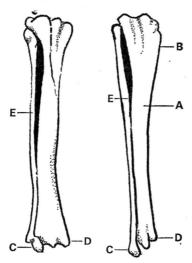

Fig. 40. The Tibia and Fibula

A. *Shaft of tibia*   D. *External malleolus*
B. *Crest of tibia*   E. *Shaft of fibula*
C. *Internal malleolus*

of the rectus femoris muscle which glides with it up and down the groove of the trochlea.

The Tibia

In the dog the tibia is normally lengthy with the hock set low down. Selective breeding has now made the tibia even longer, with the object of producing what is termed " angulation ".

The external malleolus (see fibula) is not united to the lower extremity of the main portion of the tibia. The articular furrows at this end of the bone run in an anterior-posterior direction.

The Fibula is a long and slender bone. Its upper end is articulated to the head of the tibia but its lower end furnishes the external malleolus which articulates with the lower end of the tibia but is not united with it, and it also articulates with the astragalus of the hock joint.

At their upper end there is a wide space between tibia and fibula

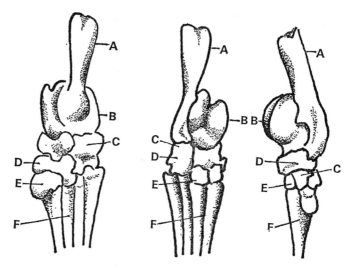

Fig. 41. Bones of the Tarsus or Hock

A. *Os calcis*   D. *Scaphoid*
B. *Astragalus*   E. *Cuneiform bones*
C, *Cuboid*   F. *Metatarsal bones*

but in their lower half the shafts of tibia and fibula are in contact and held together by fibrous adhesions.

The Hock or Tarsus

There are seven bones in the hock of the dog; os calcis, astragalus, scaphoid, three cuneiforms (inner, middle and outer) and a cuboid.

The cuboid is a rather square solid bone lying directly below the tuber calcis while the scaphoid lies below the astragalus and is a flattened bone which has to take a great deal of strain. It sometimes fractures or becomes displaced, especially in racing Greyhounds. The three cuneiform bones fit in beneath the scaphoid and between the scaphoid and the metatarsal bones of the lower limb.

The remainder of the limb below the hock is similar to that of the fore limb.

CHAPTER SEVEN

MOTION

The spine of the dog, unlike that of the horse, is very flexible throughout, so much so that the running dogs, such as the Greyhounds and their like, can actually use the loins and thighs in unison, the hind limb seeming to commence immediately behind the sacrum when the dog is galloping.

In the horse the hind feet seldom land in front of a line dropped perpendicularly from the navel to the ground but in most dogs capable of speed, the hind feet actually shoot past the elbows or shoulders to land slightly in front of the position occupied by the fore feet when the dog is standing.

It could almost be inferred by studying moving pictures of racing Greyhounds that the loins and hind limbs perform most of the propulsion and that the fore limbs are used to support the body at the termination of each leap through space and to act as spokes (as in a wheel) to take the weight as the body travels over and past its own elbows.

But even if this were the case as regards galloping at speed, it is true that the fore limbs, above the elbows, are still adding to the forward thrust of the body through space but obviously not exerting anything like as much force as the hind limbs.

At slower paces, both fore and hind limbs are active, but whether the hind limbs are dominant, or the fore, depends largely upon the position of the head, which not only brings about a change in the centre of gravity whenever it is raised or lowered, but also needs some extra and special support when it is being positioned with nose to the ground with the object of registering scent.

In this position the head is an obstacle to progress and the dog is travelling more or less blindly. This is shown when a Spaniel or Retriever tracking game by its scent, may even stumble over a

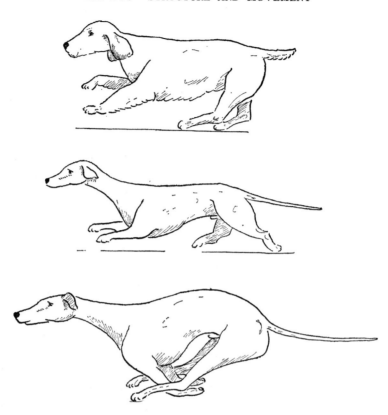

Fig. 42. Dogs in a hurry

Cocker Spaniel
Dachshund
Greyhound

dead or wounded rabbit without seeing it and then return to it
merely because the scent beyond it is absent.

The neck and head of the dog are dependent upon the fore limbs
for support but in a rather special manner.

The shoulder blades (scapulae) are attached to the ribs by means
of muscles, or conversely it may be said that the ribs and the
thorax are swung between the two fore limbs as though they were
in a cradle.

There is considerable lateral movement between thorax and shoulder blades but only a very limited up-and-down movement.

When the heavy head and neck of a hound are lowered, a considerable strain is thrown upon the fore limbs, enough to make it difficult at times for the latter to do much more than shuffle over the ground in unison with the movements of the head and neck, and merely providing support to the fore end of the body. In this type of movement most of the propulsion is produced by the loins and hind limbs.

In walking on firm, level ground as on a pavement, or when trotting with head held up, the degree of propulsion is fairly evenly divided between the fore limbs and the hind.

Dogs are of varying shapes and it follows that the centre of gravity varies according to the relative weights of the front half of the body and the hind half.

In a Bulldog for example with a very heavy head and front and a lighter rear end, the centre of gravity lies well forward and more weight falls on the front feet than upon the hind.

In a Greyhound with highly developed loin and quarters, more weight lies behind and the centre of gravity is accordingly farther back.

All this affects locomotion in the sense that the body has to travel parallel to the ground throughout its length whatever its weight distribution may be. It follows, therefore, that certain types of conformation within each breed must tend towards ease of movement and an optimum relationship between what one may term " travel " between the two main portions of the body. This relationship is the basis of what is referred to in show reports as " balance ".

Balance depends largely, therefore, upon perfect co-operation between the fore and hind limbs in supporting and propelling both halves of the body in synchronization.

The actual propulsion of the body through space depends upon two separate factors (a) the particular gait at any movement (b) acquired momentum.

Watch a terrier walking with its attendant along a level pavement. At this slow pace the body is lifted along inch by inch practically (if not theoretically) by the concerted limb movements induced by muscular contraction. The body is propelled a few inches through space by the force generated by the pressure exerted by one hind foot against the ground. During this forward movement the front portion of the body, the shoulders for example, pass over the fore limb taking weight at the time until the limb assumes the perpendicular position. From then on the fore foot associated with this limb begins to push down against the ground and as the foot recedes, the limb forms an angle with it and so the degree of propulsion increases. The body is now becoming " front-heavy " and unless the weight were quickly redistributed the dog would fall forwards, nose to ground.

This redistribution of weight is effected in two ways : (a) the hind limb (usually that of the opposite side) advances until the foot meets the pavement at about the spot where a line dropped from the dog's navel would touch the ground.

(b) Immediately before or after this happens, according to the individual gait, the opposite fore limb advances and the foot lands forward on the pavement at a spot roughly at the level of the dog's head.

Continuation of this routine movement constitutes " the walk ", actually the " slow walk " since there are marked differences between the fast walk and the slow.

In the faster paces there are moments when the fore foot is lifted from the ground before the hind foot of the same side has reached it so that instead of three feet being on the ground at one time, there will be only two.

The body then tends to roll towards whichever side at the moment provides the least support, and the head and neck may dip and rise in conjunction with the movements of the fore limbs.

At slightly faster speeds, a gait will result at which never more than two feet touch the ground at one time and the " walk " becomes the " trot ".

During the gallop there may be moments when only one foot touches the ground and at occasional moments, none at all; the body being propelled through space entirely by the momentum already created.

Briefly, the slow walk involves three-point suspension; the fast walk incurs two-point, the order being: L.H. and L.F.—L.F. and R.H.—R.F. and R.H.—R.F and L.H.

During the trot weight falls upon diagonal rather than upon opposite limbs.

The picture is now L.F. and R.H.—R.F. and L.H. For a fraction of a second during the change over of limbs from one side to the other, all four feet are off the ground.

As already mentioned the gallop in the Greyhound consists of a series of leaps mainly created by the combination of loins and limbs, the two being practically continuous, and apart from the difference in the length of fore limbs in the two animals, the gallop of the Greyhound is somewhat akin to that of the Kangaroo.

When galloping upon a circular race track the fore limb nearest the centre of the course takes the greater part of the weight and so becomes the leading leg. If by any reason the dog is thrown temporarily off its stride and changes legs, there will be a loss of speed and the winner is more often the dog that uses its brain to retain its balance and maintain the same type of gait throughout the race.

On the straight track Greyhounds tend to turn all their feet slightly towards the midline of the body but on curves or bends they lean their bodies towards the track centre at an angle of thirty-five degrees, with the feet of the inclined side turned inwards and

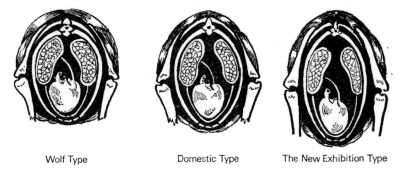

Wolf Type   Domestic Type   The New Exhibition Type

Fig. 43. Types of chest shapes on section

I

those of the opposite side inclined slightly outwards.

It must not be imagined that because a dog has good conformation it must be a good mover, even when the neck, shoulders and limbs are all that might be desired.

A great many dogs fulfil all the requirements of the most exacting standard—until they are asked to move.

There are dogs in many shapes, from the Irish Wolfhound down to the diminutive Chihuahua. They all differ in size, weight and in natural balance.

Some breeds are front-heavy; very few are too heavy at the rear end. Some have long legs and short bodies while others have diminutive legs and long bodies. All of these have to be able to please the judge by carrying their bodies in a straight line when they walk, and also parallel with the ground. All must move their fore limbs, hind limbs, feet and pasterns in orderly sequence and what is even more difficult in connection with some types of conformation, the fore feet must keep pace with the hind, and the hind feet with the fore whether they are comparatively close together with legs of respectable length, or whether the legs are short and the fore feet three feet in front of the hinder ones.

If we look at a Cocker Spaniel we will find that the height of its withers from the ground approximately equals its length of body. The limbs are of proportionate length so that when walking fast, the hind feet advance to a point fairly close to where the fore feet have rested.

Next imagine a Dachshund, very long in body and very short in limb. The stride in both hind feet and fore must necessarily be short. To put it briefly the separate pairs of feet can only " toddle ". The imprints of the hind feet must always land a considerable distance behind those of the fore feet. As there is so much intervening space the central portion of the back is not supported other than by its own muscles and spine. Unless this were true, the back would sag in its middle.

Moreover, in this breed, the fore feet (provided the dog owns a well-inclined shoulder) will tend to take a longer stride in front and the hind feet, more limited as regards movement, may have some difficulty in keeping tally with the front feet. To do so the hind limbs have to move forward a shorter distance, a little faster than the fore limbs, in order to maintain an even pace.

This upsets the rhythm of movement and creates a pattern of footsteps as seen in the snow, very different from that left by a dog of more proportionate build.

This variation in the breed pattern of footsteps is quite interesting and can be tested by wiping the pads with glycerine (quite harmless) and walking a series of dogs along a dry, smooth pavement and comparing the positions of the pad marks.

Although not so easy to record, the difference in footprints is much more marked in the various breeds at a gallop.

A dog which is accustomed to regulating its stride in order to travel over open ground may find considerable difficulty in adapting it to crawling slowly around a showring or even marching up and down over a limited space of a few yards unless it has received a considerable amount of training previous to its first show. A dog which does not shine at an indoor show may also do much better when given more space in one held outdoors.

A balanced gait is one in which there is perfect synchronization between the two halves of the body, resulting in perfect co-ordination between the movement of fore and hind limbs, with correct length of every stride to enable each foot to make contact with the ground at the precise moment.

The basis of all good movement is dependent upon an inclined shoulder which permits upright head carriage, without which the muscles advancing the fore limb cannot operate to full advantage. A dog, properly balanced, is as light on the feet as a professional dancer in contrast with the dog that moves away from the judge as though it were carrying a weight on its back.

This may be due to inequality between the natural length of the fore and hind stride, something which has been introduced as a side-effect of selective breeding but would not arise in a member of the dog family living in its natural state.

Failure to synchronize in the hinder parts may also at times be due to difficulty in flexing the spine, a condition frequently encountered in Dachshunds and in Pekingese, more commonly at least than in most other breeds.

It cannot be gainsaid when speaking of modern angulation that when a dog has a good shoulder and a free front stride, a moderate degree of angulation, or in other words a little additional length of each tibia, may improve the action as it enables the hock to flex and the hind foot advance beneath the body sufficiently to maintain balance.

There is however a difference between a little angulation and the excessive angulation which is now becoming so fashionable. The side effects of excessive angulation are only now beginning to be understood and there is a distinct possibility that in time to come it may be necessary to take steps to breed out excessive angulation to prevent the development of a race of cripples. Hip dysplasia is only one of the faults which *may* be encouraged by modern fashions in dog architecture.

Hindquarters and hind action may be affected considerably according to the angle at which the sacrum is set in relation to the ground surface upon which the dog stands.

A dipping, lowset sacrum gives rise to weak sloping quarters, a badly set-on tail and a poorly developed second thigh, not infrequently accompanied by cow hocks.

In the Terriers in which tail carriage is so important, the sacrum must lies parallel with the ground surface or even very slightly elevated at the rear end. When this elevation is not overdone, one may expect a back which appears short and an erect tail. When the elevation is excessive, the tail is apt to be " gay " and tip too far over the back.

Most judges like to be able to see the pads of both the fore and hind feet when the dog is going away, a sign that the hocks and knees are being properly flexed. Nowadays some alteration of the standard has crept in as regards Poodles and these are not now expected to stand over as much ground as previously, with the result that the feet stand more in line with the seat bone and the hind pads are not visible (or should not be) when the dog is moving away from the judge.

Normal   Wide

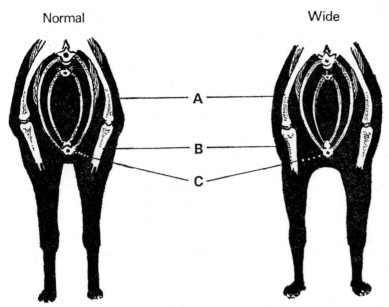

Fig. 44. Width between fore limbs

A. Scapula
B. Humerus
C. Sternum

This diagram shows the degree of width which may exist between the elbows and the fore limbs generally, and how it may vary in accordance with the degree of curvature existing in the first three pairs of ribs.

It must not be forgotten that the thorax is suspended between the two scapulae solely by muscle and is capable of a good deal of movement irrespective of simple transport. Balance, and the adaptation of the thorax to various positions such as standing, sitting, and especially the cornering carried out by greyhounds on a circular track, are all made possible by this means of suspension.

Sometimes extreme width between the fore limbs results in the feet being rotated outwards but there may be other reasons.

In the dog during movement, turning in the toes (pintoeing) may arise from excessive weight at the fore end of the body but it is sometimes a means of protection from skidding upon slippery ground. This may occur when a dog is being exhibited indoors upon a polished floor, although it might not be evident upon a non-slip surface.

The centre of gravity varies in different dogs as regards its exact position and according to whether the ground beneath the feet is level or raised at either end of the body. A

Just as the scapula should be set at an inclined angle, so should the pelvis. In the hind limb the pelvis is taking the place of the scapula in the fore limb. Insead of being erect it should be set at an angle of thirty degrees with the ground. It should be well covered by the muscles of the quarter and followed down the limb by a muscular second thigh, a point often overlooked.

It is the muscles of this region which propel the greater part of the weight of the body. The hind feet should always be sufficiently large and provided with thick pads as it is through these that power has to be applied to the ground.

The fore limbs should neither be too close together nor too far apart. When the sternum is wide and heavily muscled beneath, as it is in most of the hound family and in many of the gundogs, the elbows tend to be wide apart and there may be a tendency to turn in the toes.

The degree of curvature of the first four pairs of ribs will also determine to some extent how much space there will be between the fore limbs. The ideal is that the first three pairs of ribs shall be only slightly curved and that from then the curvature should gradually increase up to the tenth pair and then slightly diminish.

The front pasterns should retain their width from below the knee down, be firm and upright and capable of bearing weight without permitting the feet to sprawl in a forward direction.

Standards are laid down for the type of foot required in every breed.

Having written all this about structure and conformation, let us now look at the other side of the picture.

For centuries man has been endeavouring to produce the perfect dog, the perfect horse or even the perfect cow, by selective breeding.

All horses are very much alike in the anatomical sense, whether they are Shires of Shetlands. The main difference lies in size. Cattle

---

dog is more likely to pintoe when the centre of gravity is well forward, or in other words when more weight falls upon the fore end than upon the rear.

A similar condition may arise if the fore end of the body is at all times heavier than the hind.

are valuable only so far as they produce milk or beef but they still have to be bred with special types of conformation if they are to compete in the showring.

Dogs and horses are both valued for their beauty, the perfection of their physical development, their ability to move gracefully and rapidly from place to place, and also for their stamina. Incidentally, they should also be awarded marks for temperament but the confines of a crowded showring may not always be the best place to form an opinion during a few minutes acquaintance.

One can only hazard a guess as to stamina for as I have written before, the best shaped dog may not be the best worker and many of the gundogs shown today would never stand up to a long day in a mixed shoot.

Man has conceived a picture of the perfect dog and the perfect horse. He has achieved his aim on many occasions only to find that perfection of form does not ensure perfection of movement, nor necessarily any great improvement in stamina.

When it comes to speed or the ability to travel long distances in record time, the dog which would stand no chance in the showring may put up a lot better performance than the exhibition champion. We must regretfully accept it as a fact that we are all in the dog game as fanciers, aiming to produce a dog in conformity with a written standard and only in exceptional cases are we trying to produce a dog capable of doing a job of work. The exceptions may include some of the Terriers, Hounds and a few of the gundogs; not forgetting police dogs and guide dogs.

It follows therefore, that all the breeder and fancier can do is draw up a standard—or revise an old one—for each particular breed, omitting such characteristics as may favour unsoundness or deterioration within the breed, and aim at producing a dog which fulfils the requirements of its own particular standard. It has recently been shown that some of the existing standards are introducing and perpetuating faults which will have a harmful effect upon the future progress of the breed concerned. So far as stamina is concerned, no existing standard decrees that any member of any breed shall be capable of travelling such or such a distance in a specified time. All that we can insist upon in the showring is that an exhibit must be capable of walking in a straight line the length of the ring and back to the judge; that it shall conform in shape with the requirements of the standard of the breed and that in temperament it will be sufficiently intelligent to refrain

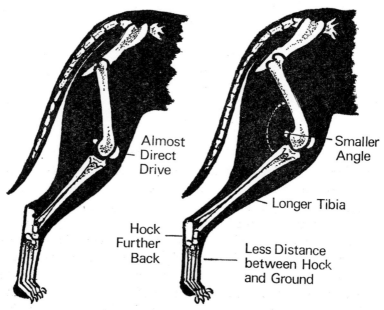

Fig. 45. Angulation

<table>
<tr><td align="center">Normal
hind limb</td><td align="center">Limb suffering from
excessive angulation</td></tr>
</table>

In the normal limb the force travelling to the hock after application of the hind foot to the ground, passes up the shorter tibia which lies almost in a straight line with the femur. The force is applied from the head of the femur almost directly into the acetabulum.

In the over-angulated limb, now in fashion, the tibia meets the lower end of the femur at an angle so that direct drive cannot ensue and the femur can only transmit the force to the acetabulum after the rectus femoris muscle has contracted, thus enabling the femur to assume some degree of joint rigidity in its connection with the tibia.

In the original straight hind limb the line of force impinging upon the circular acetabulum was directed on to what may be termed a 10.30 position. In the angulated limb it is changed to nine o'clock and the femur which normally rotates in the acetabulum in clockwise position; now tends to proceed anti-clockwise.

from biting the judge before he or she has made the awards.

The only breed asked to do more than this in the showring is the Alsatian, which is required to show off its paces, especially on the turn, as well as its own special conformation. This, too, is the only breed that tests the stamina of its handler which must be at least equal to that of his exhibit. But, even in this breed, the present standard needs rather more careful consideration.

The Alsatian of today differs very markedly from the Alsatian of ten years ago both as regards the relative proportions of the two ends of the body and the degree of hind limb angulation. There is always a danger that a man-devised standard designed to produce an object of beauty may introduce other features which ultimately may prove disastrous to the breed.

In every breed it is important that both ends of the body, fore and hind, shall retain their correct proportions with the centre of gravity approximately constant in each member of the breed.

The fore limbs and the hind should co-operate in body propulsion and it is a mistake to imagine that by increasing the angulation of the hind limbs one can establish increased power of propulsion operating through the hind limbs and thence through the animal's spine.

As mentioned previously, in every four-legged animal the force derived from pressure of the hind foot against the ground has to be transmitted to the pelvis at the acetabulum, and thence to the spine, via the sacrum. This is the direct route and it involves little or no wastage of power. The argument that a man does best when he pushes a car from behind, does not apply to the dog because in the over-angulated specimen the power is directed onto the wrong part of the acetabulum, and in anything other than a straight line.

Moreover, in order to maintain the necessary degree of rigidity of the joint between the tibia and the femur, other muscles have to come into use.

Excessive angulation is being gradually introduced into more and more breeds and unless fanciers call a halt there will be much trouble in store.

The best evidence as to the truth of this theory apart from

the Alsatian, is to be seen in the modern exhibition Greyhound and comparing it with the modern type of racing Greyhound. The former has now attained a marked degree of angulation in the hind limbs with an elongated tibia.

The racing Greyhound is, as compared with the exhibition type, almost straight in hock and stifle and covers far less ground. When raced, the one against the other, the little straight-legged dog can run away from the over-angulated show dog owing to the fact that it is less wasteful to employ a shorter, straighter hind limb and a greater number of shorter strides than to employ a less number of longer strides.

Angulation was introduced on a false supposition but once it had become established it was retained because it gave a more pleasing appearance to the dog's outline.

In the terriers the back is short and the loin strong, the hind-quarters powerful, and although modern practice is tending to the production of a longer hind limb than was in demand fifty years ago, it has not yet reached a dangerous stage of angulation.

So far as their spines are concerned the most unfortunate are the long-backed dogs, especially the Dachshunds.

The abnormal length of spine between the wither and the croup is unsupported at its centre so that undue strain falls upon the intervertebral articulations and the intervening cartilaginous discs.

It has been said that the normal life of dogs of this breed is fourteen years, but the spine is good only for five years. Although Dachshunds tend to suffer at intervals from disc trouble with temporary recoveries, the tendency is for ultimate paralysis to develop at a comparatively early age. Whether this failing is hereditary in nature or if it is simply a matter of mechanical breakdown, is uncertain. In addition to Dachshunds, disc protrusion has been observed in Cocker Spaniels, Pekingese, Labradors, Scottish Terriers, French Bulldogs and Boxers, also in mongrels.

The manner in which a dog moves may be modified by various factors. These include the conformation of the individual and particularly the degree of slope of the scapula.

A dog with an upright shoulder blade usually carries the head horizontally when in motion instead of lifting the head above body level, as it should do, in order to enable the fore limb to be brought forward with the aid of the muscles which pass down the neck and are inserted into the bones of the fore limb. Chief among these is the brachyocephalicus, which is attached to the skull, and after travelling down the neck is inserted into the humerus. Contraction of this muscle pulls the leg forward.

Other factors affecting locomotion include weight distribution, the comparative weights of the fore end of the body and the hinder end, or in other words the position of the centre of gravity.

This varies in different dogs and different breeds. In the Bulldog for instance, the fore end of the body is massive and heavy but the hinder end is much lighter. Accordingly, the centre of gravity is well forward.

In a Corgi, or a Fox terrier the centre of gravity lies farther back. This means that in the Bulldog most of the weight of the body lies in front of the midline while in the other two breeds the front and hind halves weigh about the same. In the Bulldog far more weight falls on the fore feet than upon the hind and the muscles of the shoulder and thorax are called upon to do more work in moving the body than those of the loins, quarters and second thighs.

The Bulldog, like the Old English Sheepdog, is expected to walk with a rolling gait.

There is nothing gained by it because on account of its uneven distribution of body weight the Bulldog could not walk without this roll.

In the case of the O.E. Sheepdog the reason for the roll is rather different. In this breed exaggerated hock flexion causes the body to descend slightly on the side which carries the weight, while the opposite hock is being lifted.

Pacing occurs occasionally in some breeds: Salukis, Dalmatians and in a few Greyhounds in particular; the hind and fore limbs of each side advancing together.

Ambling comes midway between the fast walk and the trot. Here again the hind and fore limb of each side operate in unison. Sheepdogs are rather prone to the ambling gait.

Pintoeing is seen in may breeds and a great deal of discussion has centred around its probable cause, especially as it occurs in dogs with the best conformation, as well as in those not so soundly constructed.

In the majority of breeds, when the dog stands at ease, there is a tendency for the toes to point slightly outward rather than inward and yet such a dog may commence pintoeing when moving either towards or away from the judge.

But, if taken onto a slippery floor and asked to move forward, even the soundest dog may commence pintoeing merely because turning in the toes helps to maintain stability and avoid slipping on the treacherous surface. Some will only turn their toes in when pulling up to a standstill—a method of putting on the brakes.

Pintoeing constantly during movement, is seen more often in gundogs, especially when they are working nose to ground. Many hounds do it habitually when hunting, but may walk normally with heads up.

Dogs which travel on all surfaces with toes turned in, must be penalized in the ring, but it is doubtful whether one which *occasionally* turns in the toes to act as a brake, should be compelled to lose marks.

Dogs which pin-toe constantly may be the victims of their own anatomy and some of the reasons are as follows : —

(a) The first four ribs may be excessively curved in their upper thirds. This causes the upper end of the scapula to be pushed outward and the shoulder joints have to follow. This usually results in a corresponding offsetting of the elbow joints, and the toes then turn inward in an attempt to restore balance.

(b) The lower end of the humerus may be slightly out of place as regards its articular surface which articulates with the radius and ulna.

This can result from a rather exaggerated degree of rotation of the shaft of the humerus in the region of the musculo-spiral groove.

The result (as in [a]), is a corresponding change in the position of the elbow joint. In order to maintain balance the dog turns its toes inwards.

(c) There may be some abnormality of the olecranon fossa or a discrepancy in the width of the outer and inner parts of the articulation at the lower end of the humerus.

In the dog, the outer trochlea of the lower end of the humerus is only faintly grooved. Any slight deviation of this groove will affect the position of the whole limb below it.

This may induce the toes beneath to turn slightly inwards.

Another matter for consideration when discussing elbow position concerns the pectoral muscles which anchor the inner aspect of the arms to the sternum. In growing puppies these muscles may be under developed or slack, and they may enable the elbows to adopt the " out-at-elbow " position.

Exercise, and time for growth, usually corrects this.

Plaiting is the name given to the gait when the hind feet follow the fore feet in direct line. It is another way of maintaining balance and may be likened to the movement of the limbs of a cat walking along the top of a very narrow wall.

In some breeds, including the Bedlington, the fore and hind feet are expected to travel in direct line.

The degree of lift of the fore feet from the ground varies in different breeds.

Terriers and hounds are " daisy-cutters ", their fore feet skimming the ground but with long strides straight from the shoulder. The foot lands on its two centre nails and the weight then falls back onto the thick hind triangular pad.

An Italian Greyhound needs to travel with exaggerated uplift of the fore feet—a " mincing " gait.

Poodles travel with a long sweeping stride in front with a certain amount of uplift, not so exaggerated as in the former breed. It has been described as " fairy-like ".

Their hind action has already been described.

This brings us to the end of the recital.

Writing these lines as I am, late on New Year's Eve, I can best conclude with a resolution applicable to the kennel, whether you be owner, or merely an inmate.

" Hold your head high and stride firmly forward, happy in the knowledge that you have sound reserves behind you."

INDEX

Abdomen, 103
Acetabulum, 116, 117, 118, 119, 120, 121
Adam's apple, 73
Afghan, 47
Alsatian, 25, 27, 47, 52, 116, 137, 138
Adrenal glands, 113
Ambling, 139
Angulation, 115, 116, 117, 123, 136, 137, 138
Aorta, 74
Aqueous humour, 65
Artytenoid cartilage, 59
Atlas, 22, 68, 69
Auricles, 99, 100, 101
Axis, 68, 69

Backmating, 11
Balance, 127
Basenji, 42, 47
Basilar process, 23
Basset hound, 42, 47
Beagle, 47, 48
Biceps muscle, 77, 83, 85
Bladder, 108
Bloodhound, 47, 51
Borzoi, 33, 42, 47, 48
Boston terrier, 31, 47
Boxer, 31, 42, 47, 138
Brachialis muscle, 83
Brachyocephalic muscle, 77, 79, 139
Brachyocephalic heads, 19, 20, 25, 29, 35, 42, 43, 44, 45, 49
Brain, 26, 34, 36
Breeds recognised, 11
Brows, 48
Bulldog, 25, 31, 42, 48, 51, 127, 139
Bullmastiff, 20, 31
Bull terrier, 31, 41

Caecum, 107
Cairn, 86
Canine teeth, 44, 45, 49
Carnassial teeth, 45
Carnuncle, 63
Carotid artery, 74
Carpus articulations, 89
Cavalier, 22, 31, 47
Centre of gravity, 125, 127, 139
Cervical bones, 22, 79
Chambers of eye, 62
    anterior, 62
    posterior, 62
Cheeks, 37
Cheek teeth, 45
Chihuahua, 27, 31, 43, 45, 47, 48, 71
Chin, 49

Choroid, 62, 63
Chow Chow, 47
Ciliary body, 62
Circumvallate papillae, 57
Cocker spaniel, 48, 130, 138
Collie, 47
Condyle, 41, 49
Conformation, 12, 13, 14, 15, 130
Conjunctiva, 61
Convulutions, 27
Corgis, 47, 139
Cornea, 50, 61
Coronary band, 93
Cranium, 22, 25, 27, 28, 29, 48
Cranial capacity, 20
Cranio-facial angle, 41, 42
Cribriform plate, 29

Dachshund, 47, 84, 88, 130, 138
Dalmatian, 139
Deerhound, 48
Dentition, 43-5
Dewclaws, 94
Dewlap, 51
Diaphragm, 74, 95
Digits, 90
Dolichocephalic heads, 19, 24, 25, 27, 42, 71
Dorsum of tongue, 58
Downfaced breeds, 41
Ductless glands, 15
Duodenum, 104, 105, 106, 107
Dwarfism, 88

Ears, 50
Ears external, middle and internal, 50, 53, 54
Ear canal, 54
Ear carriage, 52, 53, 54
Ear cartilages, 53, 54
Ear drum, 54
Ear flaps, 51
Ear shape, 51, 52
Epididymis, 109
Epiglottis, 56, 59, 73
Ethmoid bone, 29
Ethmoid meatus, 40
Eustachian tube, 59
Eye, 60-5
Eye Chambers of, 65
Eyeball, 29, 60, 61-65
    Movements of, 65
Eyelids, 50, 60

Fabella, 122
Feet, 92, 93
Femur, 120, 121, 122, 123
Fibula, 123
Foetalization, 24
Foot, 90-4